WILDLIFE
FACT·FILE
yearbook

·1994·

Overleaf: *A young Sumatran elephant, one of a population of only about 200, feeding shoulder-deep in a swamp.*

WILDLIFE
FACT·FILE
yearbook

·1994

Foreword by
Julian
Pettifer
Includes an
interview with
Bill
Oddie

First published in the UK in 1993 by International Masters Publishers Ltd.
Winchester House, 259–269 Old Marylebone Road, London, NW1 5RW

Edited, designed and produced by International Masters Publishers Ltd, London.

Publishing manager	*Deborah Clarke*
Editor	*John Birdsall*
Deputy editor	*David Buxton*
Editorial consultant	*Jonathan Elphick*
Art & design editors	*John O'Sullivan & Sue Walsham*
Illustrator	*Steve Kingston*
Picture editor	*Mira Connolly*
Picture researchers	*Marian Pullen, Jackum Brown, Vickie Walters*
Production manager	*Suzie Hutton*
Production controllers	*Stefan Podhorodecki & Andy East*

Colour reproduction by Kestrel Lithographic Reproductions, Chelmsford, Essex
Printed and bound by Arnoldo Mondadori, Verona, Italy

Set in 11/13pt Garamond

Every effort has been made to use environmentally friendly materials in the
production of this book. The paper contains 50 per cent recycled fibres and was pulped and
bleached using acid-free substances. Oxygen was used in the bleaching process, avoiding the
use of environmentally damaging chemicals. The boards were manufactured from
100 per cent recycled materials.

The publishers would like to thank Hal Robinson and Dr Tony Hare
for their help and advice in producing this book.

ISBN: 0 9518566 3 4

FOREWORD

Television is very good at stimulating people's interest but not much good at analysis. There is no doubt that many young people — and the not-so-young — first felt the magical grip of the natural world through a television programme; there is equally no doubt that to continue down the nature trail they will need to do more than switch on the box. Above all, they will need to venture into the great outdoors and learn at first hand how to enjoy the wildlife experience. In this, they will need help; and that may come from friends, relatives or conservation organizations and, of course, from books.

The *Wildlife Fact-File Yearbook* is certainly one of the best produced and most accessible reference books of its kind I have encountered. In fact, there is nothing else I have seen that is quite like it. What makes it invaluable is that it constantly updates wildlife news and reassesses the issues. Even for those of us who think we keep ourselves reasonably well informed, it is useful to read a crisp summing up of the oil pollution problem or a clear analysis of the ever changing arguments over global warming.

Apart from the well-chosen words, the book contains a stunning selection of photographs which leap at you from every page. Some serve to shock, as they vividly portray the more destructive side of our nature, but most are breathtakingly beautiful. And perhaps this is key to the book's appeal: in its visual celebration of natural wonders it shows us with painful clarity exactly what it is we all have to lose.

Julian Pettifer

Above: *Well known presenter of television natural history documentaries, Julian Pettifer is also vice president of the RSNC and a Trustee of the Royal Botanical Gardens, Kew.*

Left: *Although more agile on land than true seals, eared seals such as these Australian sea lions are at their most graceful and elegant in the weightless world of the ocean depths.*

INTRODUCTION

In its previous annual editions the *Wildlife Fact-File Yearbook* has endeavoured to present the reader with a representative breakdown of some of the pressing issues facing the earth's ecosystems and global environment, the animals of the world and the individual and collective efforts that are being made to improve the state of the world we all live in.

This year, as in others, the subject features are divided up to fall into one or other of the four major sections of the book. Yet, in many ways, almost any of these subject areas could find an equal place in any of the sections, depending on the angle of approach taken in the text. What this demonstrates quite simply, and reflects very strongly, is the complex, interlinked and interdependent nature of the world at large. No creature, no habitat, no effort to examine, educate, protect or conserve can ever be looked at in isolation. For the whole is a cohesive fabric of strands, every one of which has a vital place in a wider design and without any one of which the complex pattern would begin to break down.

An example is the orang-utan. Here is a fascinating creature in its own right and one which we are only just beginning to understand more fully. As such it finds a deserved place in the section 'Animals of the World'. However, orangs are under threat and, in recognition of its plight, captive breeding programmes are under way to help ensure that numbers are maintained and so that reintroductions to the wild can boost dwindling populations. This aspect alone could fill the entire captive breeding feature which also appears in the same section. Further, orangs are

endangered because their rainforest home in South-east Asia is being lost. Again, the precise details of the effect this has on orangs' behaviour is part and parcel of the feature on forest loss in 'Environmental Issues'. Still in this section, you can find a piece on the way humankind competes with virtually every creature on earth, including the orang.

Moving on to another section, the work of the Environmental Investigation Agency (EIA) — 'the Wildlife Sleuths' — aims to expose the criminals behind the still widespread and illicit trade in wild animals. Orangs are protected by international law, but they continue to be captured and smuggled out of the forests to be sold on for huge sums of money, just because someone somewhere would like to keep an exotic pet. Although the EIA's campaign against the trade in rhino horn is featured here, its recognition of the problems facing orangs and many other animals could have figured strongly. Similarly, World Wide Fund for Nature and the Earthwatch organization both have stakes in the various campaigns to save the orang-utan.

Behind all this lies the intricate problem facing anyone trying to direct any efforts towards conservation. Equally, covering more than a fraction of what could be said and shown is far beyond the scope of a single publication. However, it is to be hoped that by focusing on a selection of highly topical issues it is possible to bring a more complete picture to light, and through words and pictures reveal something of the astounding diversity and beauty of the natural world that our carelessness is threatening to destroy.

Opposite: *Under threat. All three races of gorilla are classified as either vulnerable or endangered.*

ANIMALS
OF THE WORLD

Our predominance as a species spans a meagre timescale when measured against the millions of years that dinosaurs walked the earth. And it probably took cataclysmic, even cosmic, events to cause the global mass extinctions which ended their reign. Sharks, too, have lived on earth for longer still and in their watery fastness have proved even more resilient over time.

Now, though, after just a few generations of concerted persecution, sharks are suffering particularly badly from human predation. Similarly, Asiatic lions, orang-utans, polar bears and many birds are facing direct or indirect assaults on their survival. Captive breeding, especially in zoos, has made many advances recently and offers hope and a lifeline for these and many other creatures under threat. But the real key to the future of all animals must lie in the long-term conservation of wild habitats.

Yet as humankind continues its seemingly inexorable spread, some creatures appear to be fighting back of their own accord. The list of species joining and exploiting our own self-made habitat — towns and cities — is growing by the decade. And the signs are that the invasion will continue.

Right: *A young male African lion basks in the company of a sibling cub. Though lion populations are not under threat, the animals are no longer safe outside the boundaries of wildlife reserves.*

Below right: *Though age-old symbols of terror, most sharks are harmless to humans. But many shark species are at risk from commercial and game fishing.*

Below: *The Florida Everglades are home to the anhinga — a cormorant-like bird that spears fish with its bill.*

KINGS OF THE GIR FOREST

Opposite: The sociability of males varies markedly between the two subspecies.

Below & bottom: The Asian male has a sparser mane than its African relative.

In the north-west of India, on the Gujarat peninsula, the world's last wild population of Asian lions roams free in the Gir Forest Sanctuary. A survey in May 1990 counted a total of 284 lions in the area. With only 150 animals in zoos, the Asian lion is one of the planet's rarest animals.

Historically, Asian lions ranged across northern India and westwards through Pakistan, Iran, Iraq, the Arabian peninsula, Turkey and even Greece and the former Yugoslavia. But persecution by people soon diminished their range. The Romans captured vast numbers and used them in their games arenas and they were hunted down by the early farming communities to protect their stock. Aristotle mentions that lions were still to be found in Greece in 300 BC, but thereafter they quickly retreated towards their present refuge. The last confirmed sighting of an Asian lion outside India was in Iran during the 1940s.

The Asian lion belongs to the same species as the African lion, but both are recognized as separate subspecies, or races, as they differ externally in a number of ways. Both males and females are similar in size and colour to their African counterparts, but the mane of a male Asian lion is far less luxuriant than that of an African lion, exposing nearly the full length of the forelegs and the ears. The opposite is true concerning the tail and elbow tufts as they are more pronounced in the Asian lion. Particularly characteristic of the Asian lion is the presence of a fold of skin that runs from between the forelegs along the abdomen to the hind legs. Both sexes of all Asian lions have this skin fold while very few African lions do.

These features, along with certain skeletal and molecular variations, were once thought to be the only important differences that distinguished the two subspecies of lion, but recent field research has shown that their social systems also differ markedly.

A 'pride', or family group, of African lions is usually made up of a group of females, who are generally related, their cubs and a resident unrelated male — or in some cases two males. The male's main role is to ward off any other males which try to oust him from the pride. Should a rival male win control of a pride he will then kill all the suckling cubs in order to

Below & bottom: *The last sanctuary of the Asian lion is the 1400 sq km Gir Forest Sanctuary, India — where these pride juveniles are basking in the dappled shade of morning.*

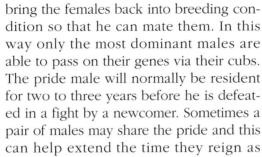

bring the females back into breeding condition so that he can mate them. In this way only the most dominant males are able to pass on their genes via their cubs. The pride male will normally be resident for two to three years before he is defeated in a fight by a newcomer. Sometimes a pair of males may share the pride and this can help extend the time they reign as they make it much more difficult for a single rival to break in. An African pride male plays no part in catching prey, but due to his greater size and strength, he will feed from the catch first, or at least have a prime spot at the carcase.

A pride of Asian lions will also be made up of related females and their cubs but no males are resident. The sexes only associate to mate, then they separate again. The males therefore hunt independently.

This quite different behaviour on the part of the males of the two subspecies may provide a clue to one of the physical differences between them. An African lion's larger mane will make him more imposing to a rival — an intimidating appearance can bluff an opponent into backing off. Should a confrontation escalate to a fight, then the thick hair around his throat will give at least some protection. Living alone, the Asian male plays no such protective role and so has no need to attack or defend itself from others of its kind — an exaggerated mane, therefore, is of no value. Why, though, should there be such a radical difference in the social behaviour of two so very similar animals?

The answer, in part, could be that social behaviour is determined by the relative numbers and type of prey species in both lions' ranges. The large, concentrated herds of game, like zebra and antelope, in sub-Saharan Africa allow for a degree of

'free-loading' by the pride male — that is, he can afford to avoid taking part in the hunt because he knows he will still benefit from the success of the females. The habitat of the Asian lion, however, is far poorer and lacks the roaming herds of the African grasslands; the Asian's fare is usually made up from small scattered herds of axis or sambar deer — prey that is harder to find and which feeds fewer lions at a sitting. Thus the male cannot rely on the females to provide the meals and so he has to hunt for himself. And if he is often away hunting he can play no protective role.

From a social standpoint, then, the Asian lion falls somewhere between the African lion and the tiger. The tiger is a more solitary animal overall as both sexes lead largely separate lives. A single male may have two or three females in his territory and the male will occasionally associate with a female and the cubs he has sired, but otherwise the adults of the two sexes do not mix or group.

Studies of the evolution of the big cats have shown that the lion and tiger branched from a common ancestor less than two million years ago, while the African and Asian lions separated as different subspecies only about one hundred thousand years ago. But just when and how the various social systems evolved is not known; and deciding which came first, the mixed-sex grouping of African lions or the matriarchal society of the Asian lion poses unanswerable questions. What is clear is that the continued protection of the Asian lion is vital not only because of the physical differences between it and its African relative, but also because it provides the opportunity to study a unique feline social system.

Unfortunately, the long-term security of the remaining wild population faces a number of threats — the main one being that the sole population lives in just one 1400 sq km reserve. Here, the increasing number of encounters between lions and the local people is giving cause for concern. Should the reserve be over-run, as happened recently in Manas National Park in Assam when villagers objected to their being excluded from using the park, then the lions could be wiped out by farmers who see them as a threat to both themselves and their animals. A single population is also in a precarious position should disease strike. If a virus, such as rabies, or feline enteritis — the main disease that all feline species are susceptible to — takes hold, then it could wipe them out in six months.

In the light of these risks, an attempt is about to be made by the Indian Forestry Commission to move a number of lions. This will

Left: *On the open African plains, big game is relatively plentiful and pride numbers tend to be greater than Asian groups. Shade, here cast by scattered acacias, is an essential component of lions' territories.*

Below: *Lionesses are tender mothers yet cub mortality is high — only 20 per cent of the young live beyond two years, largely because they starve in hard times or are taken by other predators while the adults are away.*

have the further benefit of reducing over-crowding as there is no more room in and around the Gir Sanctuary to allow the present population to expand. Over thirty years ago an attempt was made to establish some of the lions in Utar Pradesh — several hundred kilometres north-east of the Gir. They did well for a few years, slowly increasing in number, but then they all disappeared. Poisoning by locals was suspected but not proved.

Before the lions can be moved to a new area, however, three main problems must first be overcome. First, an area of suitable former lion habitat has to be found which contains a healthy population of prey animals and yet is free of tigers, which would compete with the lions. Second, the local people must be sympathetic to the idea of having lions on their doorstep. There are around one billion people in India and space to farm is at a premium, so villagers are bound to give priority to the security of themselves and their livestock over that of the lions. But without the support of the local people any reintroduction project is bound to fail, just as it did in Utar Pradesh. Third, it has to be ensured that the lions will stay where they are put, otherwise there is no point in moving them to a specially chosen area in the first place. This is a difficult condition to guarantee as translocated animals have a tendency to wander back home — stories of domestic cats travelling long distances are well documented and the same can be true for wild cats.

At the moment, the only safety net protecting the Asian lion is the captive population. This now is being gradually built up from captive-bred lions in Indian zoos. In 1990, four Asian lions were flown out from Sakkarbaug Zoo to London Zoo. These were the first Asian lions to leave India in twenty years. The point of the exercise is to start a captive breeding programme outside India as a further safeguard against extinction. Until recently, there was thought to be a sound population of about 200 Asian lions in European and American zoos, but molecular analysis of the captive populations

proved that many of the lions in the Western and even some Indian zoos were hybrids. A very prolific pair of hybrid lions had crossed with all the pure stock and so the gene pool was further diluted. Luckily, Sakkarbaug Zoo had managed its lions carefully and the stock had remained pure, enabling a new breeding programme to be started.

However, the long-term fate of this physically and behaviourally unique cat is still hanging in the balance and it will take the combined efforts of the Indian national parks, the people of India and the zoos of the world to pull it back from the very brink of extinction.

Douglas Richardson

Above: *Lions occasionally prey on domestic livestock, bringing them into conflict with local farmers*

Opposite, left: *Deer, like the chital, are favoured prey of the Asian lion.*

Opposite, far left: *An Asian lioness on the prowl in the Gir Sanctuary.*

Left: *Though the African lion is not endangered as such, it is no longer safe outside the large reserve areas south of the Sahara.*

SHARKS HAVE HEARTS

It is easy to find champions for appealing marine animals like dolphins, turtles or sea lions, but ask people how they feel about sharks and the reaction will probably be simple fear: *Jaws* has a lot to answer for. In fact, the widely held conviction that sharks are implacable man-eating monsters is vastly exaggerated. About 30 people a year die from shark attacks; elephants kill ten times that number, yet they are protected by law and considered gentle. Humans, who are also protected by law and considered civilized, kill a million sharks for every person even bitten by one and the sad fact is that many of the 360 or so shark species are now in danger.

Sharks are hunted for their flesh, liver oil, fins, teeth and skin; they are killed accidentally in nets and on lines meant for other catches; large species are hunted for sport, and pursued out of a deep-seated hatred every time a shark attack hits the headlines. Currently, the most serious threat to many shark populations is probably the growing market for shark-fin soup. Shark fins are now so valuable, fetching up to US$50 per kilo, that many fishermen no longer bother to bring home the whole carcase. Instead, they employ the revolting and wasteful practice of 'finning' — catching the sharks, cutting off their fins and throwing the maimed bodies back into the sea to die. It seems that nobody loves sharks. Yet sharks are vital members of the marine community. If they are reduced or wiped out, the balance of the marine ecosystem will be destroyed. This is particularly true of predators at the apex of the food chain, such as the great white and the mako, as well as of specialist eaters such as the horn shark, whose molar-like teeth have evolved for crunching up invertebrates such as sea urchins. Many sea urchins eat coral; if horn shark numbers are depleted, the proliferating urchins may munch their way through an entire reef and kill it.

The more that is discovered about sharks, the more vulnerable they would seem to be to the pressures of intensive fishing. Apex predators, whether on land or sea, are never abundant. They mature late and reproduce slowly as they have no natural enemies. One shark expert, Dr Keith Banister, estimates the global population of great whites, for example, to be as low as about 2000. Consequently, many scientists and shark experts are urgently seeking conservation measures to protect species which have been depleted. The

Below: *The white-tip reef shark patrols the deeper waters around reefs, snapping up its prey of fish and octopus from the seabed mainly by night.*

great white has even been proposed for inclusion in CITES Appendix I, which would place a worldwide ban on its capture. But, particularly in the case of the great white, conservationists face an uphill battle against public opinion. In Australia, where beach culture is a way of life and an important source of tourist revenue, the commonest line is still 'the only good shark is a dead shark.' Around the Mediterranean, another haunt of great whites, all sharks are regarded as vermin and a threat to commercial fisheries. There is only one place in the world where great whites have complete protection: South Africa. The legislation there came into force in April 1991; protecting great whites within 320 km of the South African coast. An interesting effect of this has been a growth in tourism: divers now travel from all over the world to encounter these formidable fish, albeit from the relative safety

Above: *Though one of the sea's most formidable predators, the great white shark may be an endangered species. A recent estimate puts the global population at a mere 2000.*

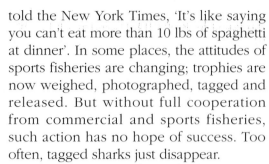

of floating steel cages. The measures are particularly surprising because the Natal Shark Board was originally set up in 1957, after an epidemic of attacks, to develop anti-shark measures. It has since become a centre for shark research with an enlightened attitude towards conservation. Although, at present, beaches around the Cape are netted to keep sharks away from bathers, the Shark Board employs 30 boats to patrol the nets and free any creatures — including sharks — which are found trapped but still living. Dead specimens are returned to the laboratory for dissection and research. Australia also has net patrol teams, but any living sharks discovered are shot on sight, regardless of whether they are considered dangerous.

In the USA, new regulations came into effect in 1993 governing the number of sharks which can be caught in a year. Weight quotas have been agreed for oceanic sharks, such as the mako and thresher, and 22 coastal species including the dusky, bull, tiger and great white sharks. Finning has also been outlawed. It is hoped that these measures will allow dwindling shark populations to recover. Sport fishing will also be limited, although many feel that the limits are too high. Dr Carl Safina, director of marine conservation for the US National Audubon Society,

told the New York Times, 'It's like saying you can't eat more than 10 lbs of spaghetti at dinner'. In some places, the attitudes of sports fisheries are changing; trophies are now weighed, photographed, tagged and released. But without full cooperation from commercial and sports fisheries, such action has no hope of success. Too often, tagged sharks just disappear.

New discoveries about sharks are constantly being made, but every piece of information seems to generate as many questions as it answers and highlights just how little is known about this ancient and varied family. Sharks belong to the subclass called Elasmobranchii, or fish with cartilaginous skeletons, which includes skates and rays. The first sharks patrolled prehistoric seas 400 million years ago, and their modern cousins inhabit every ocean except the very coldest Antarctic waters.

Top: *A lemon shark patrols a Bahamian mangrove.*
Above: *The tiny cookie-cutter shark.*

They range in size from the biggest fish in the world, the massive whale shark, which grows to more than 13 m long, to various deep-water species which reach 25 cm or less. There are sharks in the deepest oceans and around the shallowest reefs; the bull shark is even able to cross from salt water into fresh water, cruising far up rivers in search of prey.

This immense adaptability is the secret of the shark family's success and is at least partly due to the range and sensitivity of their senses. In addition to the five which are familiar to us, they have two extra senses; one which detects vibration and another which picks up electro-magnetic sources. Using special nerve cells located along the sides of their bodies, they can detect vibrations caused by movement in the water. A struggling fish, even at some distance away, can easily be located.

Comparisons have been made between the rhythmic thrashing of a wounded fish and the kick of a swimmer's legs. Such movements could well draw sharks to investigate, possibly leading to an attack.

The unique electro-magnetic sense works through a network of receptors called the ampullae of Lorenzini. These are small pores concentrated on the shark's head, which lead down jelly-filled canals to a sac lined with tiny reactive hair-cells. These detect the minute electric impulses given off by all living things (as well as inanimate electrically conductive objects). Sharks use this sense to hunt in the dark, in murky water, or when their prey is camouflaged or buried. Hammerheads and bonnetheads have been observed sweeping the sea-bed for buried fish, using their distinctive heads as a human would use a metal detector. The sensory advantage given by spreading the ampullae of Lorenzini over a wider area may have been a factor in the evolution of their extraordinary head-shape. Evidence is growing that the ampullae of Lorenzini are also used by sharks to navigate by the earth's magnetic field. Experiments on captive stingrays have shown them capable of learning, through magnetic information alone, to take food from an enclosure placed in the magnetic east of their pen, rather than an identical one in the magnetic west. Soon, the rays entered

Above: *Mackerel sharks, like this blue shark, are fast swimming, streamlined hunters. The dangerous great white and the mako shark, much prized by sports fishermen, also belong to this group.*

Left: *Once excited by blood in the water, a group of sharks will become frenzied and may take a bite at anything — even each other.*

Above: *Tagging a tiger shark.* **Opposite far right:** *The distinctive silhouette of the hammerhead.* **Opposite right:** *A tiger shark swims almost to the shore.* **Below:** *The bottom-living grey nurse shark.*

the enclosure even if no food was placed there. When the polarity around the stingrays' pen was artificially reversed, the rays' behaviour altered accordingly so that they still veered to the enclosure in the magnetic east (actually the west).

Many species of shark exist which have been seen only a handful of times because they inhabit depths of 350 m or more. The goblin shark, no great beauty among fish, with its tiny eyes, flabby, pale skin and long, pointed snout, was first described in 1898. Since then, only about three dozen specimens are known to have been caught, the largest of which was 3.84 m long. Its diet probably consists of squid and small fish; scientists believe it finds its prey by detecting any movement it makes and also by using the ampullae of Lorenzini which cover its snout. Another rarely seen deep-water shark, the 40-50 cm cookie-cutter, is not as harmless as its name might suggest; in fact it was named after its habit of biting round, biscuit-shaped chunks out of prey much larger than itself. The failure of trans-Atlantic fibre-optic cables has been traced to the bites of the cookie-cutter and its characteristic teeth-marks have even been found scarring an American nuclear submarine!

The biggest surprise of the century for shark biologists came in 1976, when an entirely new species was discovered by accident. *Megachasma pelagios* — better known as megamouth — was dragged up from a depth of 200 m, entangled in underwater gear and, sadly, dead. Its body was like that of other sharks but its great, gaping mouth, designed for feeding on plankton, was most distinctive. By 1990, two further specimens had been caught, both dead, but on 21 October of that year, a live megamouth was snagged by fishermen off Dana Point, California. Two days later, after worldwide publicity, it was released with an ultra-sonic transmitter attached. Dr Don Nelson and Bob Lavenberg were able to track it for several days and discovered that it migrated vertically to and from the depths — down to 160 m on one dive — following the flow of plankton.

Shark research is breaking new ground in many fields. Sharks' corneas are transplanted to repair human eyes and work has begun to discover if sharks carry anticancer agents. Their tough skin, which enables them to slip through water so swiftly, is also under scrutiny; military experts believe that unlocking its dynamic properties may help improve the efficiency of boat and aircraft design.

Fortunately, the bad publicity surrounding sharks in some places is being replaced by a healthier interest. In Britain, the Marine Conservation Society recently launched an educational campaign with

the slogan 'Sharks have Hearts' and, in 1993, joined forces with Sea Life Centres to create Shark Patrol, a mobile exhibition which travels to schools around the country. Elsewhere, other educational projects are being developed. They have in common the aim of separating the myths from reality and hope that they will be able to raise a wave of public sympathy for these most maligned of creatures.

Sarah Foster

Above: *The smooth-skinned silky shark is one of the most widespread and common open ocean sharks. Adults may reach 3.5 m in length.*

Above right & opposite: *The mighty mouth of the world's biggest fish — the whale shark. This harmless giant has been known to grow to over 13 m yet it sustains its 10-tonne bulk by feeding mainly on tiny crustacea and plankton.*

NET GAINS AND LOSSES

The clean pounding surf around Australia has created a whole beach-based culture, but the seas there hold one of the world's most formidable predators: the great white shark. In the 1930s, after an increasing number of attacks on bathers, protective nets were strung across the most popular bays and, in human terms, they have been a success. But the safety of the beaches has been won at a terrible cost to the marine wildlife on the other side of the nets — for they are death-traps on a gigantic scale snaring fish, dolphins, turtles and even birds with indiscriminate ease. However, a remarkable new shark barrier could bring an end to netted beaches in Australia and elsewhere. Invented by Norman Starkey and Grahame Charters, two scientists working for the Natal Shark Board in South Africa, the barrier works by sending

electro-magnetic pulses along a submerged cable which repel sharks by interfering with their electro-magnetic sense. On trial in Australia's Coral Sea, the device repelled sharks even when they were feeding. Tests are continuing to make sure the barrier works on all sharks in all waters. If it proves totally reliable, the deadly nets could come down within the next few years.

IN THE URBAN JUNGLE

Opposite: *Raccoons have now become urbanized in many parts of the USA.*

Below: *Cockroaches thrive in city warmth, while house martins relish the now cleaner urban air (bottom).*

As the end of the millennium approaches, nearly half of humankind is living in cities. And the relentless pattern of 20th-century urban growth shows no sign of abating as the world's mega-cities, such as Tokyo, Seoul, Mexico City, New York, Shanghai, Calcutta and London, continue to expand — some way beyond predicted saturation points. A recent estimate makes the year 2010 a threshold — the moment when more than half of us will live in towns and cities; the point at which the human race becomes predominantly urban.

The urban fabric gradually evolved from our social nature. Now, the hugely complex range of our activities like trade, commerce, industry, services and government imposes more reliance on, and closer contact with, one another and demands ever bigger structures to support the communal base.

But though we have made towns and cities for ourselves, one thing is certain — we are not their only inhabitants. In the same way that people gravitated from the countryside towards wealth-creating urban centres, our footsteps have been followed by a growing band of creatures — eager to exploit what our habitat has to offer.

It is just before dawn in a green suburb of a Californian town; all is quiet, people are sleeping, an occasional car glides past. Around the corner of a house shuffles a strange cat-sized animal with a long naked tail: a Virginia opossum. It makes its way across the lawn to the dustbin, but the lid falls noisily as the animal clambers onto it. Startled, it runs off into the night. The Virginia opossum was once a purely rural animal, coming face to face with humans only occasionally. But over the last few decades it has really come to town — via the farmer's chicken coop — and now raids gardens and garbage cans for food throughout much of the USA. It is one of the very few North American animals that has a wider distribution today than it did when Europeans first arrived in the New World. Its spread has been helped by escapes from zoos and by deliberate introduction, but in the main this remarkable marsupial has spread of its own accord, simply by taking advantage of a suburban habitat waiting to be exploited.

Meanwhile, in the town centre, in a small restaurant, a very different animal is carrying out its nocturnal food-gathering. Here and there on the walls and floor of the restaurant move shiny brown insects — cockroaches — their antennae ceaselessly busy, testing every square centimetre for traces of something edible. There is plenty for them to eat — even the tiniest scrap of food left behind in a crack provides these industrious insects with a

Right: *Brown rats have thwarted all attempts to remove them from urban centres for centuries. It is a sign of their remarkable tenacity and adaptability that the latest idea to combat them is a 'genetic missile' capable of producing infertility in whole populations. But there is some concern that such a powerful biological weapon may backfire.*

Below: *Large numbers of Brahminy kites can be found around the harbours and refuse dumps of India and South-east Asia, squabbling with crows for the best scraps and even picking over unburied human corpses.*

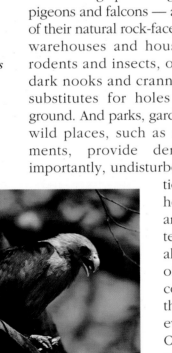

banquet. The owners despair: they keep a spotless kitchen, yet despite repeated fumigatations it is only a matter of time before the 'roaches return.

At first glance there may seem to be precious little in common between the opossum and the cockroach. But we are now learning that they do, in fact, share a great deal. And what is emerging is a fascinating picture of typical urban dwellers. But why do some animals join us and not others? The simple answer is that in creating a habitat for ourselves we also unwittingly recreate conditions that are also ideal for many other species.

Like us, all animals have the basic needs of shelter and food: cities readily provide both in abundance. Sewers are perfect for damp-loving rats; the sides of tall buildings provide good nest sites for pigeons and falcons — as artificial replicas of their natural rock-face homes. Factories, warehouses and houses are ideal for rodents and insects, offering countless dark nooks and crannies that are good substitutes for holes in trees or the ground. And parks, gardens and untended wild places, such as railway embankments, provide dense and, more importantly, undisturbed cover. In addition, cities generate heat and hence the ambient year-round temperature is usually higher than that of the surrounding countryside. Within the buildings this is even more marked. Consequently, in temperate regions, animals originally from warmer climes are able to establish themselves in urban areas. Cockroaches, for instance, are tropical insects, but have managed to extend their range by exploiting the warmth of cities in regions where they could not otherwise survive.

As far as food is concerned, urban environments provide a varied and abundant supply. Every bit of rubbish, from street litter to that piled up in huge municipal dumps, will be investigated by one animal or another. Urban wild animals do not just eat products that we think of as food; they choose from a wider menu. Mice, for example, have even been known to eat glue and candles. Cockroaches can find even easier pickings — it is known that they can survive for years on end in the

back of a warm and cosy TV set, gleaning a living from the dust and nibbling at the insulation on electrical wiring. Waste or undeveloped land can offer a cornucopia for birds and insects, for where ground is left to lie untidy and unweeded, important foodplants can spring up which may be difficult to find in the increasingly well manicured countryside.

If abundant food and shelter were the overriding factors that attracted wildlife to our urban environment, then doubtless towns and cities would be as overcrowded with a wide variety of animals as they are with people. As this is conspicuously not so it can be guessed that at least most creatures are more than a little wary of vying with the planet's supreme predator in his own backyard. But not all are quite so respectful. By circumspection, cunning and opportunism, many of our urban lodgers are able to outwit our ability to discover them or foil our best attempts to eradicate them. The potential non-human city-dweller must therefore possess certain special qualities.

There is no hard-and-fast rule about what makes an animal a suitable candidate for success in the urban environment, yet it is easy enough to draw up a profile based on their essential qualities. Typically, these creatures tend to be small to medium-sized, highly adaptable, unspecialized, fast-breeding omnivores. Size is important and perhaps places the greatest constraint on any creature looking for an urban niche. It must not be too big, or there will be nowhere for it to hide. It may be, or may need to become, nocturnal or crepuscular (active at dawn and dusk) to avoid us at our busiest and most alert; it should definitely be able to breed fast and colonize new sites rapidly. It must also be highly flexible in its approach to food, for the same diet may not be available from one day to the next.

From this profile it is easy enough to recognize many of the animals that already make the grade: cockroaches, mice, foxes, pigeons, gulls, Brahminy kites and raccoons. But perhaps the ultimate urban denizen is the rat which has lived alongside us for thousands of years. This creature is adept in every area that is necessary not only for it to survive, but to thrive: even today there are said to be a million more rats in London than there are people. They will eat virtually anything we waste; they live both under and above ground; they are inquisitive and intelligent and they breed prolifically.

Animals that currently exploit the urban fringe, like the opossum and raccoon, could, given time, easily move down

Below At home in the city: the rhesus macaque shows little fear of human residents in many Asian cities. Indeed, it actively seeks out settlements and will brazenly rob homes, stalls and shops of almost anything edible.

Above: *Though not truly urbanized, grey squirrels have extended their natural woodland habitat to become common residents of gardens, parks and green spaces in a great many British and North American cities.*

Right: *Within the range of the leopard, suburban homes are increasingly being visited by this big cat — often on the look-out for a new prey species: domestic dogs.*

town and become true city dwellers. Raccoons naturally live mainly in damp and woody places where they feed on frogs, crayfish, nuts and fruit. But they are not averse to living near people and have moved into many urban areas in the USA and Canada where their dustbin raids, like the opossums', cause much annoyance. Other animals are attracted to the edges of town but will never bridge the gap between suburb and centre; perhaps fortunately in some cases, as it is alarming to discover just what may be lurking in some suburban gardens.

In recent years some African cities, such as Nairobi, have seen perhaps the most unlikely intruder of all: the leopard. The very presence of such a creature so close to town is disturbing enough, but the motive for this visitor prowling the suburbs does even less to endear it to the local residents. For the leopard seems to have acquired a particular liking for dog-meat — and dogs are plentiful in suburban homes. The leopards have even been known to enter houses and drag off the family pet for their dinner.

Not all urban wildlife is necessarily dedicated to only one sector or another. Many species, notably birds, move around freely, grabbing feeding and nesting opportunities where they can. Towns and cities also tend to contain plenty of semi-natural habitats, like undeveloped open spaces, parks and even patches of captive

countryside which have been left untouched but which have become surrounded by urban development. These sites attract species that would otherwise find no place amongst the concrete and steel. Some birds, butterflies and squirrels, for example, are widespread in many cities but are in no way truly urban. In the very centre of Kuala Lumpur, Malaysia, there is an island of rainforest on a hill called Buckit Nanas. There leaf monkeys swing among the branches and birdwing butterflies swoop across clearings within sight and sound of 'KL Jam', the traffic snarl-up that affects the city twice a day.

Most people are not accustomed to looking for or seeking out the wildlife in towns and cities, perhaps believing that the environment must be too hostile to

attract anything more interesting than the ubiquitous pigeons and house sparrows. Yet in London, one of the very first places where urban wildlife was studied, a remarkable range of animals has been found. In a western suburb, for example, there is an established population of ring-necked parakeets; and deep in the city, not far from the old Battersea Power Station, the white letter hairstreak flits among garden and park greenery — one of around 20 butterflies that have been recorded within the city limits. Gulls and kestrels are quite common and house martins have returned to town, hawking for insects over the city squares. House martins, notably, have arrived in central London in the few decades since measures were taken to clean London's air and rid the city of its infamous smogs.

What of the future then? Are more animals likely to join us in the megacities of the 21st century? Certainly there are species that appear to have the necessary qualifications and seem to be high up on the waiting list. In the USA, the Texas armadillo, or peba, appears to be invading suburbia, just as the raccoon, opossum, chipmunk and coyote did before it. In Africa, the common palm civet, a tough and wily little animal, is increasingly seen around towns and villages; it too is a contender for a city niche in the future.

Perhaps in the next century, as wild habitats continue to shrink, cities will at last come to be recognized as rich and valuable ecosystems in their own right.

Dr Tony Hare

Top: *Red foxes make frequent raids on urban dustbins, often under cover of darkness*

Above: *Untended waste ground and industrial land quickly throw up weeds, many of which are foodplants for butterflies, like this small tortoiseshell.*

ZOOS FOR THE FUTURE

This decade is proving to be one of dramatic change for the world's zoos. Twenty years ago, a few pioneers began to see that zoos would come to play a vital role in the conservation of animals by breeding endangered species. Ten years ago, the idea took root and most of the world's major zoos were becoming increasingly involved in serious captive-breeding programmes. Now, there can be no doubt of zoos' future importance in making a contribution to preserving biodiversity. Without captive breeding, many animals, particularly large mammals, such as rhinos, tigers and Asian elephants, would probably become extinct over the next few decades; so too would many birds, reptiles and amphibians — and even some fish, insects, spiders, and snails.

Ideally, captive breeding should never be more than a back-up for protection in the wild. After all, there is little point in maintaining zoo populations of creatures which have lost their natural habitat. Captive breeding does not ignore this — it is a complement to, not a substitute for, habitat conservation.

This approach is illustrated perfectly by zoos' current efforts to save the tiger. All tigers belong to just one species but there are several subspecies, or races, which need to be conserved separately. Just 100 years ago there were eight subspecies, but three have now gone extinct: the Caspian, from Persia; and the Bali and Javan from Indonesia. Disgracefully, the Javan race was allowed to disappear as recently as the 1970s. The remaining five subspecies are all at risk in the wild.

The problem is that man is squeezing the tiger for space. Tigers prey upon big animals and each cat needs a huge territory. Furthermore, wild populations cannot survive for long unless at least several hundred individuals are present — as smaller populations become weakened by inbreeding. A viable population of tigers, that is, one which is likely to thrive indefinitely, requires an area the size of a small American state or a large British county. But all tigers live in Asia, and Asia has become a very crowded continent.

Below: *Loss of habitat due to human activity restricts the chances of the slow-breeding giant panda recovering its numbers in the wild. Remaining populations are now both small and scattered.*

Left: *The Siberian tiger is the largest of the five subspecies and may reach a weight of 300 kg. Longer fur and a broader snout are its other distinguishing features. There may now be less than 250 of these animals left in the wild.*

Above: *Many of the remaining 30,000 Asian elephants are neither truly wild nor domestic: they are working animals in logging camps. Traditionally, working cows are left in the forest to be mated by wild bulls, but now there is very little forest left for wild elephants to live in.*

Right: *The Arabian oryx was reduced to a handful of individuals by the mid 1960s, but from a few captured specimens, Phoenix Zoo, Arizona, built up a captive herd. Eighteen of the zoo-bred animals were released in Oman in 1980 and there are now more than a thousand in the wild.*

Today there are not more than 2500 wild Bengal tigers in India, most of which are in reserves set up under the 'Project Tiger' scheme during the 1970s. Although the total number may appear high, the individual populations in each reserve are mostly too small to be viable. Similarly, there may be as many as 2000–3000 Indo-Chinese tigers; but they are also too scattered to be viable. Only 500 Sumatran tigers remain at most and, again, they are widely scattered. Wild Siberians number only about 250, while the South China population stands at around 40.

Help is at hand, though. At a meeting in Edinburgh, Scotland, in July 1992, zoo biologists agreed to establish the Global Tiger Plan, whereby all tiger subspecies would be bred in zoos with the aim of supporting the wild stock. The plan is bold and ambitious and many difficulties will have to be overcome if it is to work.

The first task facing conservationists is housing several hundred captives to ensure healthy breeding. Zoos must therefore pool and swap their animals so that they form a single population, even though they are scattered over the globe. The major zoos, excluding China's, can house around 1000 tigers, which is only just enough. At Edinburgh it was agreed to leave the Chinese to look after the South China tiger — perhaps helped by the Japanese, who are playing an increasingly important role in the zoo world. Thus the 1000 known spaces can be used for the other four subspecies. The plan, then, is for European zoos to look after the Sumatran tiger, and for US zoos to establish a population of the Indo-Chinese tiger

as a back-up for captive and wild conservation in South-east Asia. India will continue to look after the Bengal sub-species — probably with back-up in Europe; while the world's captive Siberian tiger population — which now stands at 500 — is too large, and needs to be cut to make way for other subspecies.

The European plan for the Sumatran tiger further highlights some of the complexities that zoos have to face. Breeding of Sumatrans in Europe is coordinated from London Zoo, but the key to the Global Plan is a new breeding centre at Taman Safari, in Java. In time, this will act as a conduit between captivity and the wild. Presently though, it has to capture some wild stock from overpopulated reserves to widen the genetic variety among Javan and European captives. Eventually, the captive-bred animals, enriched by the new genetic mix, will be released into the wild. But at present there

are problems with Europe's zoo Sumatrans: of the 92, some are inbred and many are closely related, so although the world population is low, it will actually be necessary to get rid of some of these to make spaces for 'new blood' from unrelated wild stock.

Precariously placed though they are, tigers do at least breed well in captivity. Giant pandas are equally endangered but are very poor breeders in captivity; only 26 were raised in the decade up to 1991 and estimates put the global total at fewer than 1000. Pandas are close relatives of the bears — so close that they are often included in the same family. Bears, however, are carnivores while pandas have evolved to survive mainly on bamboo, which they digest very inefficiently because they still have the gut of a carnivore. Furthermore, all the bamboo of a species flowers and dies every few years;

Above: *By the beginning of the 20th century, the European bison, a lighter, less stocky relative of the American bison, had been largely eradicated outside Russia. But over the past 14 years two dozen captive-bred herds have been successfully reintroduced, notably in the forests of Poland.*

time ever in captivity. They did this by removing one twin to be bottle-fed while leaving the mother to suckle the other — and then changing the two babies around. But bottle-feeding is not a perfect solution as cubs grow up too tame to be released and this technique worked only because the particular female was tame; but it shows what can be done.

Another big mammal in deep trouble in the wild is the Asian elephant: numbers stand at around 30,000, which may seem a lot, but the populations are small and widely scattered. Zoos outside India may not be able to establish herds big enough to sustain the species if the wild elephants disappear. But American and European zoos are now learning to breed elephants well. Previously, one of the main problems was simply to provide enough bulls, for bulls

Above: *Fifteen years ago the lion tamarin faced imminent extinction through loss of its Brazilian rainforest home. Following a breeding programme in the USA captive numbers grew greater than those in wild populations and the tamarin has now been reintroduced to parts of its former range.*

Right: *The Bali starling occurs only in one small part of the island of Bali, east of Java, and has declined rapidly in recent years but reintroduction schemes have helped boost viable numbers.*

the pandas then lose their food supply and wild populations, already isolated in pockets by human pressure on their habitat, face starvation and decline.

Outside China, captive breeding of pandas has not been very successful simply because zoos have too few animals. Females like a choice of mates and will not accept any male that just happens to be available. Prospects would also be brighter if pandas bred more quickly and although they often produce twins, usually only one survives. However, the Chinese achieved a small but important breakthrough in 1992. At Wolong, the biggest Chinese reserve, extremely skilful handlers persuaded a female to raise both twins — for the first

are dangerous and not all zoos can handle them. More significant, though, is that European zoos as a whole have now formally agreed to help and are developing techniques, such as artificial insemination, which could be of great value given the problems with bulls.

Captive breeding is not only important for big animals: some tiny animals need help too — like the Pacific Island snails of the genus *Partula*. In 1967 an entrepreneur introduced a giant African land snail called *Achatina* to Tahiti in the Society Islands to farm for food. On different islands others followed suit. But the achatinas escaped, multiplying to become so common that they could be collected by the barrow-load. So between 1975 and 1978 the French government (which administers the Society Islands) introduced a predatory snail called *Euglandina* from Florida, to eat the achatinas. The euglandinas, however, ate the small native partulas instead. Now there are euglandinas on many Pacific islands and on every one the partulas have become, or are nearly, extinct. The island of Moorea, near Tahiti, is typical. In the 1960s it had seven species of partula. Now it has none.

In the 1960s, scientists studying partulas began breeding the snails in captivity. Today, some of those captives are all that are left of their species. In the late 1980s, a breeding programme began, the first ever for an invertebrate, coordinated from London Zoo. So far, 20 species have been bred, including six of the seven Mooreans; the seventh is extinct. The hope is to reintroduce at least some of the snails, once the euglandinas have been cleared out.

The early 1990s, then, have seen a few encouraging signs for the protection of wildlife that continues to falter under increasing human pressure. Captive breeding itself may not provide the overall solution, but the valuable back-up it offers at least gives some hope for the future.

Colin Tudge

Left: Research into partula snails led scientists to breed them in captivity. This move saved many partula species from extinction in the wild after natural populations were wiped out by an introduced predatory snail.

THE FLIGHT OF THE CONDOR

Across the world, several species have now been successfully reintroduced after they had been wiped out from the wild. One significant first-time reintroduction in 1992 was of the California condor — a huge New World vulture — which once flourished right across North America. By 1980 there were only 25 to 30 birds left in California: in 1986 the last egg laid in the wild was doomed from the effects of DDT poisoning. In 1987 only three birds remained so they were taken to join 24 captives in the San Diego and Los Angeles zoos. They bred well in captivity and by 1992 the population was large enough to risk reintroduction. But there was a problem: condors do best when they hunt in groups, because they each watch what the others are doing, and so find

prey more efficiently. Young birds also learn from their elders. So how could a new wild flock get started if only a few birds could be released, and with no mature wild birds to lead the way? The answer was to release two captive-bred California condors in the company of two Andean condors — a similar but unendangered species. The approach worked so well that by late 1992 the two 'helpers' were captured, leaving the California condors to begin a new population.

IN SEARCH OF NEW SPECIES

Below & bottom: *Researcher Charles Munn located the first blue-throated macaws ever seen in the wild .*

If you were asked how many animals, completely new to science, had been described over the last couple of years, the chances are that your answer would not even be close. Estimates in the hundreds would fall far short; even guesses up to 5000 would be way off mark. For over 8000 previously unknown species and subspecies were revealed in last year's listings alone. Some 4000 of these were insects and most were from the tropics, where new species are commonly found. But this accounts for only 50 per cent of the total — surely there can't be thousands of other animals waiting to be discovered? Wasn't everything caught by the great Victorian naturalists? The answer, it seems, is a resounding 'no'.

By the combination of inspired hunches, strenuous effort and meticulous research, together with a mandatory slice of good luck, today's fieldworkers are still finding birds, frogs, fish, and even mammals, never before known to science. And it is not only new species that crop up each year; often animals thought long extinct are chanced upon, and others are 'rediscovered' after an absence of many years. All this demonstrates the sheer diversity of life on earth and points to there being far more pieces to the puzzle than had ever previously been thought.

Dr Gary Stiles, from the Columbian Institute of Natural Sciences, is one such 'species sleuth'. An exceptional biologist, he seems to have an uncanny ability to find new and rare species of birds. He has recently discovered the Cundinamarca antpitta — a podgy thrush-like bird that lives in cloud-shrouded Andean forests — the fourth new antpitta to be found. The first was found by Peter Kaestner who was at the time the US Consul in Bogota. While exploring along a newly built road, Kaestner heard an unfamiliar call in a patch of undisturbed forest. An avid bird enthusiast, he taped the song and then played it back. Filled with curiosity, its singer obligingly hopped into view. To the diplomat's great excitement he was unable to identify it. A few months later, he and Dr Stiles returned to the forest and managed to find the bird again; then they were able to confirm that it was, indeed, new.

Not all new bird species are as easily established as the antpitta. This was certainly the case with a new species of warbler from central China — the Szechwan leaf warbler. Identification was made particularly difficult because it shares its coniferous forest home with the yellow-rumped warbler. The two are almost exactly the same size and their plumage is almost identical. But it was the song that eventually gave the game away to the Swedish scientists Per Alström and Urban Olsson. So different are the two calls that the birds pay no attention to tapes of each other's songs. Once aware of this, and clued in to minute plumage differences the zoologists also found dietary and feeding discrepancies. Later, in the Beijing Natural History Museum, they found that other scientists had been unable to distinguish the two birds by eye, for stored in a drawer, alongside a yellow-rumped lookalike, lay

a specimen of 'their' new species, which had been collected in 1962.

Sadly, some species seem fated to be discovered close to the point of imminent extinction, often because they are only revealed when most of their habitat has been stripped away. The Rungwen Mountains of southern Tanzania were once covered in unbroken forest. With different types of forest occurring at different altitudes, the whole area exhibited remarkable botanical variety. In recent years great chunks of the forest have been destroyed and continuous forest is fast disappearing. It was in such an area that the intrepid Belgian biologist Jan Stuyck found a rather unusual shrew. Trapped in the bamboo zone halfway up one of the mountains, it had thick woolly fur and a very hairy tail. Stuyck thought it might be unknown so a specimen was sent to Europe for identification, where shrew experts Rainer Hutterer, from Germany, and Paulina Jenkins, from the UK, quickly confirmed Stuyck's opinion. As a highly specialized forest form, the shrew is unlikely to be able to adapt to new habitats if its forest home disappears. Accordingly, Hutterer and Jenkins named the shrew *Crocidura desperata*, in recognition of its

Above: *In 1993 a new clingfish species was added to the 150 already known.*

Below: *The newly discovered Cundinamarca antpitta.*

Above: *Dr J MacKinnon of WWF with skulls of the Vu Quang ox, showing the sharp, oryx-like horns. A skin found later shows the coat to be rich brown with some bold black and white markings. However, a live specimen of this creature has yet to be discovered.*

Right: Nannopsittaca dachilleae, *a parrot, has recently been named but the full extent of its Peruvian range is not yet known.*

plight and published its description not in a scientific journal devoted to the classification of animals (as is usually the case) but in one concentrating on conservation.

Not all the new mammal species found on land were as tiny as the shrew. In Vietnam's Vu Quang Nature Reserve, an area of pristine forest described as a 'lost world', a combined team from the Vietnamese Ministry of Forestry and World Wide Fund for Nature discovered some strange skulls with horns and hair attached. At first sight the remains did not look particularly exciting, but they were crawling with maggots, indicating that the creature was recently alive. On closer examination, however, it was realized that they had something special. The remains seem to belong to an animal about the size of a goat that no one apart from a few local villagers has ever seen. Further expeditions discovered more remains, including an almost complete skin. The skin was later stuffed to give an idea what the animal may look like and it appears that it could be a primitive bovine related to cattle, antelope, goats and sheep: as such it has been provisionally named the Vu Quang ox. If the living creature is tracked down it will be the first large land-living mammal to be discovered for over 30 years and only the sixth to be found this century. Other discoveries by the

expedition included a new fish, tortoise and bird and all these finds have prompted the government to enlarge the reserve and ban logging in the region. So, whatever the status of the mysterious animal its future should be safer than before.

By far the largest new species to be discovered last year was a beaked whale. Peruvian whale expert Julio Reyes recognized it as different from the 12 other known species of beaked whale and named it the pygmy beaked whale, since adults of the new species are, at about three and a half metres long, somewhat smaller than their relatives. To date little is known about how the whale lives; all the ten specimens known to Dr Reyes came from waters off Peru and had either drowned in nets set to catch sharks or else were found stranded.

The sea still holds many secrets but it gave up another one in 1992 with the discovery of a living graptolite, one of a group of animals thought to have become extinct 300 million years ago, long before dinosaurs walked the earth. Graptolites must have been abundant in ancient seas, for they are one of the most common fossils of that period. Floating in the upper oceans and sieving tiny particles from the

sea they formed beautiful branching colonies. This discovery was shared between two people, Professor Noel Dilly of St George's Hospital Medical School, London, who was responsible for the analysis, and Dr Michel Roux of the French Marine Biological Centre, who found the animals 250 m down in the waters around New Caledonia Island in the south-western Pacific. What Dr Roux discovered looked like small orange blobs coating the surfaces of the tubes of deep sea worms. Professor Dilly then showed that they were a type of cephalodiscus — 16 of which were already known — and belonged to an odd group of creatures called the pterobranchia, but unlike all other known cephalodiscus species this one was colonial. Effectively, Roux and Dilly's discovery established a missing link between the known cephalodiscus species and graptolites, and this consequently led to the reclassification of all species of cephalodiscus.

All this perhaps puts a new perspective on today's endangered species in that if more new species are found than are driven to extinction, why worry? But the real point is that though the natural world seems to be getting bigger, the physical world is becoming smaller. And although our shrinking of many previously wild and unexplored habitats is revealing a growing list of new species, almost certainly we are

also unwittingly wiping out even more creatures before they have a chance to be discovered, and before their roles in the chain-links of life are assessed. It therefore takes no stretch of the imagination to see that as long as we strive to protect the natural world, every corner of it, from earth to air and water, will continue to reveal more of the secrets surrounding its interlocking, seemingly unending diversity.

Adrian Barnett

Left: *Friedrich Diertelen of the State Museum of Biology, Stuttgart, discovered this new species of striped grass mouse in the dry, tree-spotted grassland of the upper Nile, Sudan.*

WHERE ART MEETS SCIENCE

Defining a new species is not as straightforward as may be imagined, for no set rules apply. Classification is often hotly debated, even by specialists, as definition is an area where art meets science. Yet it is of more than academic interest, for accurate classification along with a knowledge of a species' distribution helps conservationists identify which animals are priorities for protection.

Different species are usually observably different from one another because they have evolved in different circumstances — as a golden eagle, for example, is clearly different from a house sparrow. On the other hand, members of the same species usually resemble each other closely in terms of shape, colour, size and diet and can breed together. Some species though, look identical to others yet possess hidden internal differences; for example, in the number or construction of their chromosomes as this may prevent cross-breeding. Such a situation has been found in Demidov's bushbaby from West Africa. Originally thought to be a single species, it is now known that there are three forms: externally, they are identical, but each has genetic differences and cannot interbreed. The scientist who made this discovery claims that this bushbaby is therefore represented by three full species.

All populations of a species vary, but if in a geographically defined population all individuals are sufficiently different from all others elsewhere, then the population may be defined as a separate subspecies, or race.

MAN OF THE WOODS

Opposite: *Heavily jowled cheeks characterize a big male orang.*

Below: *The most arboreal and solitary of the great apes, orang-utans live, eat and sleep almost exclusively in the tree-tops.*

Once a very mysterious animal, the orang-utan has recently been the subject of several extensive studies and, though many questions remain, it has become clear that it is a highly complex creature, greatly moulded by its forest environment. But the orang's home is under increasing threat and the future looks uncertain for this remarkable ape.

'Orang-utan' originates from a Malay phrase, meaning 'man of the woods'. The name is appropriate for alone among the other great apes (the gorilla, two types of chimpanzee and man), it spends almost all of its time high up in the canopy of the lowland forests of Southeast Asia, feeding there during the day and at night sleeping in a nest made of leaves.

Apart from ourselves, orangs are the only great apes found outside of Africa and are now exclusive to the islands of Borneo and Sumatra — though they were once much more widely spread. The two populations have not had any contact since the last ice age, when falling sea-levels united these great islands, and they are now sufficiently different to be regarded as separate subspecies.

A standing male comes up to the shoulder of a man and weighs between 60 and 90 kg. Both sexes have very long arms — with a span of up to 2 m — for tree-top locomotion, but only the male has the big throat pouch which acts as a resonating chamber to help project his territorial 'long call'. Adult males also have very long hair, which enhances their aggressive displays. Living for about 35 years, they are mature by the age of ten and a female may give birth to three or four young in her lifetime.

The structure of the throat means that, like chimpanzees and gorillas, orang-utans are incapable of making the complex sounds that human speech requires. However, work in the 1960s with chimpanzees and in the 1970s with gorillas had shown that it was possible to communicate with great apes using sign language. This ability seems logical given that chimpanzees and gorillas live in social groups and therefore need the facility for complex communication (even if they have yet to invent their own version of sign language in the wild). But orang-utans spend very little time together as adults. Since they have so little need to, could these apes communicate at all? This was the prompt for Dr Lyn Miles and her team from the University of Tennessee, Chattanooga, to set up 'Project Chantek', an eight year investigation into the language learning abilities of Chantek, a male orang-utan. This research has helped give a clearer understanding of the orang-utan's behaviour and its needs in the wild.

Studies with other apes had used almost a classroom approach to teaching, but Dr Miles wanted Chantek to grow up to learn a language much as a human child does. In the course of her study, Dr Miles has made some exciting discoveries.

Above: *Dr Lyn Miles and the subject of her pioneering studies — Chantek, a young male.*

Opposite, right: *A young captive-bred orang learning to live in the wild as part of a rehabilitation project in Sabah, Borneo.*

Right: *Chantek playfully gestures under his arm — the sign for 'tickle'.*

Chantek learned over 140 signs: he even invented some of his own, and used others in novel combinations. Some of these were quite sophisticated, such as 'eye-drink', when his eyes itched and he wanted an eye-bath. Less than a quarter of the signs were for food and drink. He learnt signs for actions, various types of animals, people, places, colours and emphasizers, such as 'more'.

The project's aim was not simply to get Chantek to develop a big vocabulary, however, as this sometimes backfires on investigators when their supposedly 'clever' animal fires back any old sign until it hits the one wanted. Dr Miles' aim was to let Chantek learn only the words he wanted to learn. This had odd consequences now and again; for example, he loved being picked up or carried and so learned the sign for 'up' very quickly. But, as he hardly ever wanted to be put down, it took over a year for him to learn this sign. He could also put signs together to make phrases. These were usually two or three signs long. That this was real communication, Dr Miles is in no doubt, for nearly 90 per cent of the time it was Chantek that began a 'conversation'. These could last for up to eight turns, and there was no doubt he enjoyed them.

Significantly, Chantek also used other objects to sign with, such as the blades of scissors instead of his hands, to make the sign for biting. In doing this he showed he understood that the 'sign' was an abstract representation of something else and not a particular series of movements associated with an object or action. Chantek did not just use his hands to sign either, he used his feet too, probably, according to Dr Miles, because as a tree-living creature he regarded his feet as just another set of hands.

In learning, Chantek experienced many of the same difficulties that a small child has. He had big problems with the concepts behind 'you' and 'me', preferring to use names instead. He also over-extended the meaning of some signs; for instance, 'dog' was used for almost all furry animals. Once he signed 'dog' when a very noisy helicopter flew by, perhaps because the whirling rotor blades sounded like barking. Similarly, 'bug' was used for a variety of things; not only cockroaches, beetles and slugs, but also tiny pieces of dry cat food and small bits of faeces. Chantek may have been using the sign to mean 'small inedible things'. More positively, it became clear that he understood the idea of an action, making the sign for 'break' both before (to a biscuit) and after (to a toy) the event.

One of the most exciting discoveries was that Chantek could lie. He was

encouraged to keep himself clean and would be given access to a bathroom and lavatory when it was needed. But, he loved to play with water and would signal 'dirty' even when he was clean just so he could get access to it. Once, while out walking, he took a pencil from the pocket of one of the researchers and put it in his mouth. When asked to give it back he opened his mouth, which appeared empty, and signalled 'food-eat'. The pencil was later found concealed in his bedding. This ability to deceive reveals premeditation and an ability to formulate predictions about the outcome of a request or action.

Just what, then, does Dr Miles' work tell us about the way in which Chantek sees the world? It certainly shows that he can categorize the world around him, but as his 'bug' sign shows he sometimes uses different reference points from us in order to pigeonhole things. 'Eye-drink', for example, shows that a drink is not exclusively a liquid that goes into the mouth so much as a liquid that comes in a small container. And 'open' simply means 'make object available' — as in 'open rope'.

Chantek scored well when faced with the standard tests by which the intelligence of human children is measured. By the age of 7 years 6 months he was equivalent to a 21 to 30 month-old human, and was able to point to specific pictures, fold paper, put pegs in a board and demonstrate an understanding of the concept of self. Dr Miles' detailed studies showed that the way in which Chantek learnt sign language was similar to that of human deaf children, if a little slower. Above all, though, they revealed that Chantek had the capability for abstract thought. This, according to Dr Miles means, '...that there is not only a brain but also a mind in the head of the orang-utan'.

Studies by Jargen Lethmat in Germany have shown that captive orangs can even

flake stones to make tools similar to those which primitive people used. Orangs seem to possess equal abilities to their famous tool-using cousins, the chimpanzees, yet rarely use them in the wild.

Why then is the orang-utan so clever? Being a solitary creature in the wild, isn't it brighter than it needs to be? Such questions have spurred other orang-utan specialists to look at their field notes again. Two main ideas have been proposed: either orangs are more social than was previously thought or certain factors like food finding have promoted intelligence. Birute Galdikas, Professor of Primatology at the National University, Jakarta, may have some answers.

From her base at Tanjung Puting, in the rainforests of Indonesian Borneo, Professor Galdikas has spent the last 20 years studying wild orang-utans and probably knows more about them than anyone else alive. She points out that orangs are very eclectic feeders, having observed them eating 317 different foods, mostly fruit and leaves. Contrary to popular belief, however, the rainforest is not one vast buffet from which food may be plucked with ease. Not every tree has new leaves or ripe fruits at the same time, so the supply

of foodstuffs is irregular both in time and place and is spread over a wide area. The orangs, therefore, need to remember where food is located and also have an idea of when it might be ready for eating. Given all the different types of tree in the rainforest, this calls for a considerable memory.

Yet orangs manage it. According to Professor Galdikas, 'They have very effective shortcuts to reach hidden foods and in this they seem better at navigating through the forest than primatologists following cut trails and equipped with compasses and maps.' Further, it would seem that the orangs also stop to check trees, to see how they are getting on. This has led to the development of a powerful spatial memory, and the result, says Professor Galdikas, is that 'In a single day, an animal is able to find a number of productive stems of the same rare, irregularly distributed plant species in its patch of forest.'

Professor Galdikas believes that the development of this faculty would have stimulated wider mental development as well as problem solving capabilities.

So, if food gathering has helped the orang to become clever then just how much has its social development further contributed to its latent intelligence? Professor Galdikas thinks that the orang's sociability has

Above: *Despite weighing up to 90 kg, adult orangs can comfortably support their bulk on their immensely strong arms.*

Opposite: *Babies cling tightly to their mother's long fur — even when asleep — leaving the parent's hands free for maximum mobility in the forest canopy.*

Left: *Leaving its safe haven in the trees, a male orang makes a rare visit to the ground.*

been underestimated. She points out that social interactions between orangs are difficult to observe because they occur high in the canopy, shrouded by dense foliage. But she does have evidence that orangs do associate now and again and that they remember these encounters for many years. She also believes that there are features of the orang's mating system that may have led to the development of an intellect.

A female gives birth every eight years or so. When she is receptive, males come from far and wide to court her. The intense competition between males can result in vicious fights. Generally the larger male wins. This has led to the evolution of ever larger males, so that now adult males are, on average, twice the size of adult females. This poses a problem for a female, not because her mate might hurt her, but because of the harassment she may face from sub-adult or sub-dominant males. Unable to compete with the largest dominant males, yet desperate to mate, these individuals will try forced copulations; sneaking into the female's nest at night or ambushing her on her way through the tree-tops. As the female cannot fight off such males, she has to outwit them. Strategies include behaving confidently (as if a consort male were nearby), throwing dead branches, or developing the genital swelling possessed by a mated female. If all else fails, she will run to the nearest dominant male for protection. But as the way may be long she needs a good sense of direction and because there will be several males in the area she needs to know which one to go to. All this, says Professor Galdikas, requires a devious intellect. So, it would appear that both food and sex have been important in the evolution of intelligence in orangs.

But despite its intelligence, the orang has no answers to the threats posed by humans, especially the ongoing destruction of its habitat. If such depredations continue then the future of the species may lie with those orangs which are part

Below: *Orangs build a sleeping nest each night from leaves and branches bent to make a shallow hammock.*

of well-established captive-breeding programmes or in rehabilitation stations, such as those at Sepilok and Semengo in Malayan Borneo, Ketambe in Sumatra and Tanjung in Indonesian Borneo.

At the last count there were some 578 orang-utans in captivity. But can such conservation programmes really help? Some experienced orang-watchers contend that they cannot. Many of the rehabilitation stations appear to have developed into tourist attractions rather than centres for serious conservation. And while such centres encourage support for conservation, they also increase contact and familiarity with humans which is counter-productive to any worthwhile rehabilitation programme. Some experts believe that by drawing attention away from the real threat of habitat loss, such centres actually do more harm than good. In addition, the number of orangs successfully reintroduced into the wild is so small that it can never have a major impact on the conservation of the species. Furthermore, there is also the risk that orangs raised near to people might even transmit human diseases to the wild population with disastrous consequences.

Perhaps the most damning criticism of reintroduction programmes, however, is that they are so expensive. The cost of one new scheme has been put at around US$400,000. If such a sum were spent on one of the area's national parks it would not only benefit a greater number of orangs but also all the other species with which they share their forest habitat.

Clearly, the orang's survival in captivity is no substitute for its continued existence in the wild, not least because a captive existence ignores the fact that it is the forest which has shaped the orang-utan in every way. The only satisfactory long-term answer is to ensure that we protect enough forest to support large populations in perpetuity. If we cannot do this then we will have failed one of our closest living relatives.

Adrian Barnett

LUMBERED BY LOGGERS

In the past a major threat to orangs came from their collection by zoos and for pets. Though this has diminished recently, orangs still find their way to Korea where, despite clampdowns, they are traded for thousands of dollars. But the greatest threat now comes from logging in the rainforests of Borneo and Sumatra, scenes of some of the world's most extensive deforestation. In the lightly supervised concession areas orangs are killed for food or trophies and most of the babies being traded have also been traced back to logging camps.

Worst of all, though, is the loss of habitat and food supply. Adult males need at least 4–6 kg of food every day and to find it in logged areas the apes must continually redraw their mental maps of the forest. Many animals simply move away from disturbed areas and when this happens refugee orangs then have to compete with those already resident in an area, which upsets the social balance. The dominant males, feeling threatened by the newcomers, spend more time making territorial calls, which can create a false impression: some logging companies have recently used call data to 'prove' that logging is beneficial, claiming that it increases the number of orangs present! In fact, logging means less food, more stress and, critically, fewer places for orangs to live.

AFTER DARK

Opposite: *The barn owl's superb hearing helps it to home in on its rodent prey on the darkest of nights.*

Below: *In contrast to the barn owl, which may hunt in twilight or by day, the North American flammulated owl is strictly nocturnal.*

Very few of the world's 9700 or so species of birds are truly nocturnal, that is, typically perform all their activities, from feeding to breeding, at night. In fact, probably less than three per cent of all species fall into this category. Even that most famous family of the night, the owls, whose seemingly supernatural senses have made the birds synonymous with the dark throughout the world, now appear to be less nocturnal than was believed. Nonetheless, many birds do exploit the darkling hours for a variety of reasons.

Despite the popular conception, it is likely that only half, and perhaps less than a third, of the world's 135 species of owls are normally exclusively nocturnal. The rest fall into three groups: those that are typically active both in twilight and at night, those that are active both in twilight and during the day, and those that are active mainly or entirely during daylight.

Owls have also long been thought to possess some kind of sixth sense which sets them aside from other birds. But recently, researchers have begun to realize that although owls do have very acute senses, they are only a little more acute than those of many other higher vertebrates, including our own species. Key behavioural adaptations therefore play a very important part in enabling owls, and other birds, to live at least part of their lives after dark.

There is no doubt that owls can catch prey at very low light levels. To produce the necessary bright image on the retina, an owl's eyes are exceptionally large; in the North American screech owl, for instance, their combined weight relative to the bird's body weight is greater than the total relative weight of the brain in an adult human. Their unusual tubular shape may be a modification of the normal flatter eyes of daytime birds that has resulted in a lightweight structure essential in a flying bird which at the same time produces the sharpest and brightest image possible in dim light. Yet recent experiments with tawny owls have shown that although owls' vision is, on average, slightly more sensitive than our own, there are individual humans with more sensitive eyesight than individual owls. Compared with the daytime-living pigeon, the owl's visual sensitivity is about 100 times greater, but compared with that equally nocturnal hunter the domestic cat, the owl's vision is, on average, about 2.2 times less sensitive, although, as with humans, there is an overlap, and some individual owls have better night vision than some cats.

It is a myth that owls are blind in sunlight: many species hunt prey by day, and all can see perfectly well during the day. Even a highly nocturnal species such as the tawny owl has colour vision, although it probably cannot discriminate between colours as well as a pigeon, and the owl is not so sharp-sighted by day as a human or daytime bird of prey. To cope with the dramatic adjustment between night and day vision, owls have a huge range of aperture (pupil size) controlled by the iris.

Right: *Many waders and
wildfowl, like these snow
geese, migrate by night
and day, making 24-hour-
plus non-stop flights
between Arctic breeding
grounds and winter
quarters.*

Below: *Potoos have a huge
gape to catch large flying
insects by night. Big eyes
suggest that vision is
important and bristles
around the bill probably
detect and trap prey.*

Just as their eyesight, though very sharp, has been found not to be 'super-sensitive' so the hearing of owls, though very acute, is now known to be no sharper than that of humans or other higher mammals such as monkeys or cats. Researchers have proved that owls can detect and capture prey in total darkness solely by homing in on the sounds it makes, and much of their hunting in woodland must be done by flying 'blind'. Evidently, owls cannot rely on vision alone to guide them at the very low light levels sometimes experienced beneath the woodland canopy. Interestingly, owls have been found to suffer more natural bone fractures than birds active only by day, which strongly suggests that they are more often involved in accidental collisions with objects at night. Also, owls startled by humans have been known to fly into branches or even tree trunks. On the whole, however, owls do manage to survive and hunt with deadly accuracy on the darkest of nights, so other factors must play their part.

For a long time scientists have realized that knowledge of our environment influences sensory perception. A good example of this relates to car-driving at night. People often drive at or beyond their limits of vision by relying on their knowledge and experience of a familiar car and stretch of road. This is why road works and other hazards must be so well indicated, to reduce the chance of an accident. It now seems likely that nocturnal animals, such as owls, may find their way around a familiar wood in the blackness of night by relying on similar knowledge. In this context, it is significant that the owl species that live a strictly nocturnal lifestyle in woodland (such as the tawny owl and Ural owl in Europe and the spotted and barred owls in North America) are resident all year round within the same strongly defended territory, which is used for hunting as well as breeding. Restricted to relatively small territories, they take a wide range of prey, which they catch by pouncing from a perch. It seems that they must gain intimate familiarity with their local patch over a number of years to acquire the hunting skills to ensure they and their offspring survive. By contrast, owls that live in, or at least hunt over, more open habitats — such as the widespread short-eared and barn owls, the snowy owl of the Arctic, or the long-eared owl of Eurasia and North America — need a breeding territory but do not need to defend a hunting territory year-round to survive. Without the need to build up a detailed map of a restricted

warbler, that make long sea crossings. Many migrants seem to adopt a different pattern of daytime and night-time migration at different stages along their route. Some birds migrating between nesting grounds in Europe and winter homes in Africa have to cross the vast wastes of the Sahara Desert, which extends some 2000 km from north to south. These migrants include many small perching birds such as yellow wagtails. Flying at a cruising speed of about 30–40 km/h, they would take 50–70 hours to cross the Sahara. Research shows that before they embark on their northward spring migration, yellow wagtails build up enough fat by intensive feeding to fuel them on a 50–70 hour non-stop flight, that is, a flight lasting three nights and two days. On their return journey in autumn, there is evidence that they fly at night and during the early morning, but rest in the shade of rocks or at oases

Below: *Relatives of potoos and nightjars, frogmouths are also nocturnal hunters, but catch insects and small vertebrates on the ground.*

Bottom: *One of the world's three nocturnal species of parrot, the rare kakapo.*

territory, they can travel widely in search of prey outside the breeding season. They can also concentrate on a narrower range of prey and often hunt on the wing as well as by perching and pouncing.

In contrast to owls, nightjars, kiwis and other regularly nocturnal birds, there are many birds that are nocturnal for only part of their lives. In terms both of the total number of species and the numbers of individuals, night migration is by far the most common nocturnal behaviour of birds. But the picture is more complex than was once thought. Through analysis of bird migrations it seems that most 'nocturnal' migrants may also travel by day and, moreover, that no birds migrate exclusively by night. Observation has shown that within a single species, such as the European starling, some individuals may migrate by day and others by night. In other species, most individuals seem to migrate continuously day and night for at least part of their journeys and this applies especially to small perching birds, such as the northern wheatear and blackpoll

Above: *The oilbird of northern South America and the Caribbean uses echolocation to navigate in the pitch dark of the large caves in which it breeds. It is the world's only nocturnal fruit-eating bird.*

migrate at night, though various reasons have been suggested by researchers. For example, the birds might use the setting sun to orientate by and then use the fixed pattern of the stars; this might be easier than continually compensating for the movement of the sun during the day. Night flying also avoids predatory birds such as falcons. Another advantage may be that local atmospheric conditions at night can make flight easier. Horizontal winds tend to be slower then, so birds are less likely to be blown off course. Also, air temperatures are lower than during the day and humidity is often higher, so that night migrants would not lose so much water from their bodies by evaporation. Finally, because it is cooler, the night air is denser, so a bird does not have to expend as much energy in generating lift by flapping its wings. However, despite apparent advantages, there are serious hazards too: low-flying night migrants are more likely to collide with obstacles, including power cables, and large numbers of migrating birds can die when they are attracted to strong, sun-like artificial light sources, such as lighthouses, and crash into them. Overall, it seems that there are no overriding advantages to nocturnal migration. Only when faced with a long crossing of sea, desert, mountains or other inhospitable terrain or difficult atmospheric conditions during daytime are birds forced to fly at night.

during the hottest part of the day — which reduces water loss by evaporation. When they are encountered migrating past British bird observatories however, yellow wagtails are mainly daytime fliers. It seems, then, that this species flies by night to cross the major barrier of the Sahara, but then makes a series of shorter 'hops' by day during the rest of its journey.

It has proved difficult to find a simple answer to the question of why some birds

Some birds are renowned nocturnal songsters. In North America, for instance, the northern mockingbird and the wood thrush are noted for their fine singing. Many members of the rail family also sing or call at night, including the fast declining corncrake of Europe and central Asia, which once kept countryfolk awake with its rasping song in many parts of rural Britain. But the most famous and best studied night singer is the European nightingale. The males are justly praised for the beauty of their song, an intense outpouring of loud notes, some clear, musical and bubbling or trilling, and others harsher and slurred. In the depths of the night this remarkable song sounds particularly loud in the absence of competing sounds from other birds and human activities. Many people do not realize that the nightingale also sings during the day, but those who do have long believed that this bird really does sing better at night. This has recently been backed up by scientific research.

By carefully analysing nightingale song, ornithologists have demonstrated that their night-song is more sustained, more variable, and contains longer phrases, including some rarely heard by day. The research has also shown that night and day singing perform different functions. Male nightingales tend to return from Africa to their European breeding woods before the females, and at first sing only during the daytime. This song is aimed at warning off rival males and establishing territorial boundaries, and when this is accomplished, the males start to deliver their more complex song at night to attract the newly arrived females to mate with them.

There is much to be discovered about how birds live at night. Unravelling the complexities of this fascinating subject brings together research by a wide range of scientists — from biologists or physicists analysing animal senses to field ornithologists and ecologists studying shearwaters on remote islands, kiwis or kakapos in New Zealand, or owls in British woods. Whatever they discover, though, the sudden hooting of an owl or the ghostly, floating flight of a nightjar will continue to fill us with curiosity — and a sense of wonder about lives lived after dark.

Jonathan Elphick

Above: *That supreme night-time singer the nightingale is sadly declining in Britain and other parts of Europe.*

Below: *Skimmers can feed by night as well as by day, locating fish by touch sensors in the elongated lower mandible of the bill, which, in flight, is held just below the waterline.*

DEATH OF THE DINOSAURS

Right: *With its triple horns and bony neck shield,* Triceratops *proved more than a match for the mighty* Tyrannosaurus rex. *But neither of these terrible lizards had a defence against the climatic or environmental changes which wiped out most of the dinosaurs at the end of the Cretaceous period.*

Below: *Fossilized teeth of a mosasaur — a marine relative of the dinosaurs — that probably fed on ammonites and other marine creatures. Mosasaurs and their prey species became extinct at the same time as the dinosaurs.*

O f all the 'terrible lizards' which once walked the earth, the truck-sized *Triceratops* is one of the best known. Nine metres long, this fearsome beast carried three massive horns on its heavily-armoured head and a bony shield above its neck. As well as these formidable defences, *Triceratops* was also remarkably fleet of foot, able to outrun any predator it dared not confront. But while Triceratops proved itself to be a match for the voracious *Tyrannosaurus rex*, it had no defence against the unknown killer that wiped out the dinosaurs 65 million years ago. That it battled bravely, however, is testified by the fact that it is the last of the dinosaurs to occur in the fossil record before their mysterious mass extinction.

The dinosaurs were not the only creatures to die out at this time; the period is marked by wider mass extinctions, and theories that seek to explain just why dinosaurs disappeared must also take this into consideration. Other groups which suffered a mass demise include the ammonites, marine plankton and relatives of the dinosaurs, such as the marine plesiosaurs and mosasaurs. But some creatures survived: birds live on today, descendants of the small carnivorous saurischian dinosaurs, as do other descendants of the period such as lizards, and mammals.

All the action in this prehistoric mystery takes

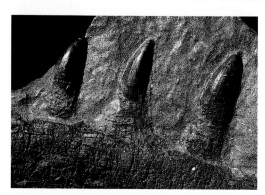

place at a boundary of geological time around 65 million years ago — where the outgoing Cretaceous period meets the incoming Tertiary period. Lately, more and more clues have been gleaned from this time, though much of it is still open to interpretation by palaeontologists.

Palaeontology is, in many ways, the study of the natural history of the past. A group of these 'time explorers' working in Montana, USA, has recently studied a huge collection of fossils. The results show that of over 150,000 specimens of 112 species considered, as many as 65 per cent survived the extinctions at the Cretaceous-Tertiary boundary. This seems to confound one of the main reasons why

geologists originally drew a line at this point — because of the great difference between the fossil animals and plants in the two periods. So, if some creatures survived while others became extinct, what was to blame?

In rocks of this age there is evidence of gradual climatic change. Rock sections in the USA show this starting some 10 million years before the end of the Cretaceous period. Initially the Cretaceous period was warm and supported luxuriant vegetation and many cold-blooded dinosaurs. Towards the fateful boundary, however, the climate seems to have become cooler with the result that temperate woodland developed together with many species of

Below: Tyrannosaurus rex *reconstructed — to reveal an 8 tonne, 15 m long beast. No complete skeleton has yet been found but it is believed that* T. rex, *a denizen of the late Cretaceous period, was the largest land carnivore ever to have lived on earth.*

small warm-blooded mammals but fewer cold-blooded dinosaurs. But why did the climate become cooler? There are a number of possibilities. About 110 million years ago continents began their most recent episode of drifting. The Atlantic began to open as South America split away from Africa. This probably led to a rise in sea levels worldwide, and shallow seas may have flooded over much of North America and Africa. The circulation of ocean currents and wind systems, so influential on climatic belts, would at first have been only subtly altered by such events, but within a few tens of millions of years considerable changes, as catalogued in the Cretaceous strata, would have occurred. One of the most susceptible groups to such change is ocean plankton — and the 'chalky plankton', like most dinosaurs, became extinct. A great number of dinosaur species existed

COLLISION COURSE?

The history of time is littered with the mass extinctions of land and marine life. Just why this should happen is not fully known, but there is evidence in the earth's crust to suggest that the earth is bombarded by bodies from space every 26 million years or so, causing global devastation. This could be due to cycles of galactic activity. It is believed that comets gather in the Oort cloud, in an orbit 14.5 million million km from the sun, and that periodically some are shaken out to reach the inner solar system. There are a number of ways in which this might happen but, if the Oort cloud displacement runs true to its past periodicity, given that the last mass extinction occurred around 30 million years ago, we could be facing a cosmic collision in the not too distant future.

during their 140 million year reign but there were probably only a few species alive at the same time and there was a general decline over the last few tens of million years anyway, so the theory of gradual climatic change has many followers. However, the boundary rocks have recently revealed clues which may show what really sealed the dinosaurs' fate.

The element iridium is very rare in the rocks of the earth's crust; it occurs mainly deep down in the planet. Yet in Italy's Apennine mountains is a sequence of Cretaceous and Tertiary limestones sandwiching a one centimetre thick layer of clay which is amazingly rich in rare iridium. So how did it get there? Could terrific volcanic activity have thrown it up?

In the Deccan area of India the largest outpourings of the dark volcanic rock called basalt erupted in the few hundred thousand years before the Cretaceous-Tertiary boundary. In all, over a million cubic kilometres of lava spewed from the bowels of the earth. At the same time there was intense volcanic activity in the USA and the south-east Atlantic, and all this may have released the iridium. The effects of such intense vulcanism would

Above: *The late Cretaceous period witnessed* Pteranodon *riding thermals over the oceans on 7 m wings and diving to scoop fish into its toothless jaws.*

Below: *Any explanation of the extinction of the dinosaurs must also take account of the parallel extinction of the common sea-dwelling ammonites — shell-bound animals up to a metre across.*

have been devastating to life on earth as the various gases, with which we are all too familiar today, poured into the atmosphere: sulphur dioxide causing acid rain; carbon dioxide, the main 'greenhouse effect' gas; and chlorine, which contributes to the formation of holes in the ozone layer shielding the planet from deadly ultra-violet rays. This suggests that 65 million years ago the earth, and therefore the dinosaurs, may have faced climatic change on a gigantic scale and relatively quickly too. Recent evidence from the 1815 explosion of Tambora, Indonesia, shows just what can happen. This eruption threw sulphur dioxide into the atmosphere, cooling the climate. Crop failure was widespread and in some places farmers spoke of the 'year with no summer'.

Another theory that seeks to explain the presence of iridium is that a huge iridium-rich extraterrestrial body hit the earth 65 million years ago, producing enormous amounts of dust to darken the sky, again with devastating consequences for the climate. If it fell in the sea, massive tidal waves, called tsunamis, travelling at great speed, would have washed over the coastal areas, and great clouds of steam and vapour would have filled the air. The effects would have lasted for months, or even years, destroying food-chains by killing plants, which rely on sunlight. The creatures best suited to survival may have been small scavenging mammals, reptiles and crocodiles, rather than most dinosaur species and other more specialized

Below: The 'terrible claw' that gives Deinonychus *its name refers not to its grappling-hook fore-claws — though these are remarkable enough — but to the huge, sharp hind-foot claw that may have been used for piercing the flesh of prey.*

animals. So what evidence do we have for such a devastating meteorite impact?

The iridium level is consistent with what might be expected if a body about 10 km in diameter hit the earth at great speed. Its impact would probably be of an order equivalent to 110 megatonnes of TNT and this would have left a huge crater. So, at hundreds of sites across the world where Cretaceous-Tertiary rocks occur, the search began. At many likely sites geologists found strange particles of two distinct types. The first were tiny rounded grains, called 'spherules'. Though made of

secondary minerals, which have replaced the original material, these are thought to represent tiny glass droplets formed by the melting of rocks caused by the impact of a meteorite. These would have sprayed out and spread over a huge area. The second type were grains of the common mineral quartz, but they had a puzzling internal structure. They seem to have been fractured, as if by shock waves from an impact. In the USA, evidence from the Rockies pointed to a crater near Manson as being the impact site, but this proved far too small, suggesting a meteorite only 4 km across. Evidence from Texas, however, provided plenty of hard facts which suggested a marine impact somewhere in this region. Here, researchers found a series of rocks, including one layer containing fragments which had been torn off older layers — as if by tsunamis that followed an impact occurring somewhere further to the south. As similar rocks also occur in the Gulf of Mexico region, this area appeared to be a strong contender. However, the rocks here are deeply buried under layers of younger strata. Thus the geologists had to use a number

Right: Stegosaurus, *the 'roofed reptile' takes its name from the bony plates on its back. It is thought that these may have been temperature-regulating devices which were used, for example, in a similar way to an elephant's ears — which are fanned to cool its blood.*

Opposite: *The sun setting over a dinosaur's footprint suggests a symbolic and enigmatic farewell to some of the most successful and varied creatures ever to have walked the earth.*

Below: *The reconstructed hatching* Parasaurolophus' *head betrays no sign of the extraordinary elongated crest for which these dinosaurs were noted. Birth from eggs, though, was common to all dinosaurs, and some theories explaining their demise point to the rise of egg-eating mammals.*

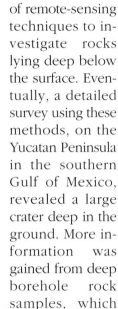

of remote-sensing techniques to investigate rocks lying deep below the surface. Eventually, a detailed survey using these methods, on the Yucatan Peninsula in the southern Gulf of Mexico, revealed a large crater deep in the ground. More information was gained from deep borehole rock samples, which had been taken by oil companies test drilling for oil in this region in the 1950s. The samples contained a rock similar to lava, but taken from a great depth. Recent closer examination has shown it to be a strange rock composed of much natural glass and shocked quartz — as would be expected from a great impact. Further, the younger rocks lying above the glass-rich material contained Tertiary fossils. When the size of the Yucatan Peninsula crater was measured it appeared to be over 180 km in diameter; quite large enough to have been made by the impact of a body over 10 km wide. On the local continental shelf much limestone had previously formed and this would have been vaporized by the impact to carbon dioxide, possibly causing acid rain and global warming. Across the Gulf of Mexico from Yucatan, at Mimbral, there is what geologists have referred to as a 'key exposure' of strata which geologically echo events at Yucatan and may prove the impact there. Only last year were exact ages for these rocks worked out. The figure of 65 million years has been obtained for samples of glass from Yucatan and elsewhere in the region — precisely the date of the fateful Cretaceous-Tertiary boundary.

There is, however, much evidence of other, though far smaller, impacts across the world. A crater at Popigay, in Siberia,which measures 20 km across exactly spans the 65 million year mark, and the Manson crater, in the USA, is also of exactly the right age. All this may point to a rain of meteorites which hit the earth at about the same time, spelling disaster for many life forms.

So, both the many clues and the hard evidence provide support for several theories. At present, though, there can be no firm conclusions except that the climate appears to have worsened considerably during the late Cretaceous period. If the dinosaurs fell victim to such events it would not be surprising.

Chris Pellant

ICE BEARS OF THE ARCTIC

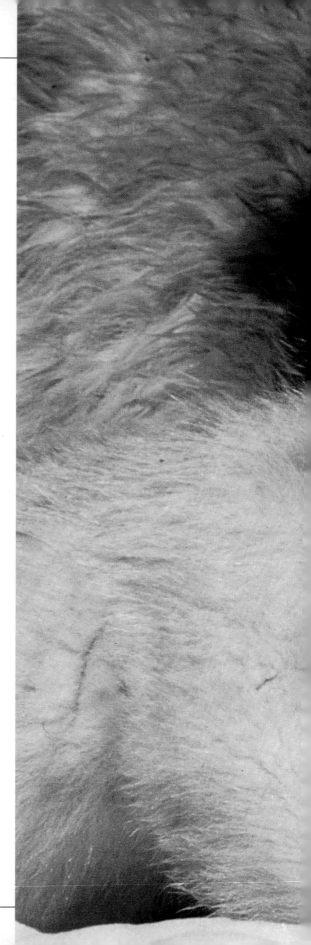

Polar bears, more than any other animal, symbolize the far north. They are masters of the high Arctic — an inhospitable, forbidding land of extremes — from the round-the-clock darkness of winter to the month-long sunshine of summer. Yet in this place where humans struggle to survive, the polar bear thrives, superbly adapted to the icy environment. In fact, polar bears exist nowhere else and may soon be facing threats to their survival for the very reason that they rely on an ecosystem increasingly at risk from pollution and worldwide climatic change.

Concern for the polar bear has been growing since the mid-1960s when wildlife biologists studying the Arctic first became worried about the numbers of bears being killed by native polar peoples and sport hunters. At the time, no accurate biological data existed to determine the status of polar bears, whether or not the bears killed were part of a single population, or even whether the kill rates were excessive. There then followed an international initiative geared to learning more about these creatures and this has been instrumental in providing a better insight into the bears' behaviour as well as helping to identify what is needed for the species' long-term conservation.

November 15, 1993, marked the 20th anniversary of the signing of the International Agreement on the Conservation of Polar Bears and their Habitats, originally drafted

Right: *Polar bears have enjoyed some degree of protection since 1938 and though current populations are healthy, there are concerns that pollution of their Arctic home may seriously threaten their future.*

Below: *True grit: shaking down after a snowstorm in temperatures of minus 40°C.*

by scientists from the USA, Canada, the Soviet Union, Norway and Denmark — the five countries which share polar bear habitats. The Agreement was ratified by the five governments in 1976 when it took effect, and reaffirmed in 1981 for an indefinite period. It has proved to be a remarkable case of multinational cooperation. Protection of the arctic ecosystems on which the bears depend was a vital part of the Agreement too and important habitats high in the Arctic Circle — in Svalbard, Russia, Greenland and Canada — were defined. Hunting is now prohibited in much of these ranges and is carefully controlled elsewhere.

It is not known exactly where or when polar bears first appeared as the fossil record is sparse. The oldest polar bear fossil — a leg bone less than 100,000 years old — was discovered near Kew Bridge, England. But palaeontologists believe they evolved less than 300,000 years ago from brown bears in a part of Siberia that became isolated by glaciers. Here, brown bears would have found the most abundant food out on the ice; indeed, grizzlies still wander out on to the sea-ice today. Researchers recently captured a large male grizzly feeding on seals hundreds of kilometres north of normal grizzly bear range in the Canadian Arctic. Cut off from the mainstream populations, the brown bears rapidly evolved from generalized omnivores into specialized predators. Selection favoured lighter-coloured, hollow guard hairs, dense underfur, sharper teeth and claws, larger well-furred feet and a streamlined body. Other evidence supporting this evolutionary root has come from new genetic research and the fact that, in zoos, polar and brown bears have mated and produced fertile offspring.

Polar bears are highly intelligent animals and though they are strong and heavy they are surprisingly agile for their

huge size — more than twice the bulk of lions or tigers. Large males can weigh up to 700 kg and stand 1.5 m at the shoulder. They are long-lived too; one male kept at London Zoo lived for 41 years, though in the wild the record is 32 years, while on average females live only 12–14 years. Polar bears are slow to mature. Females do not produce cubs until they are 5 or 6 years old and may have only 1 or 2 cubs every 3 to 4 years (4 to 10 cubs in a life-time). They mate in spring but the fertilized eggs do not implant in the womb or develop until autumn — and then only if the female's fat reserves are sufficient for her to den, give birth and nurse her cubs.

Females dig a den in a snowdrift around the end of October. Many polar bears den on land in traditional areas — some of the major denning sites include Svalbard, Wrangel and Churchill. In parts of Alaska females may den out on the drifting sea ice. Radio-collared females have been tracked drifting in ice dens for over 1000 km. Even at outside temperatures of minus 50°C the den temperature remains relatively warm. The cubs are born around late December and weigh under 1 kg each, but by the time they

emerge from the den in March or April their weight has risen to 10 kg. When fully weaned at about two years old they may weigh in at 180 kg.

Polar bears are tireless walkers and strong swimmers. Recent satellite data shows that they may wander at least 5–6000 km in the course of year. Before radio and satellite tracking showed otherwise, bears were thought to wander randomly around the Arctic, moving with the ice that itself is subject to winds and currents. But, as more and more bears were marked and collared, biologists recognized that relatively distinct, regionalized populations exist.

Physiological studies of general bear hibernation have also produced some remarkable new insights into polar bear behaviour. Most members of the bear family that hibernate do so in response to a lack of food, not because they cannot cope with winter weather. But unlike black and brown bears that den during the lean winter

Above: *Threat posturing may escalate to a fight when the normally solitary bears compete for food.*

Opposite: *Dense fur keeps out the cold while furred footpads help keep a sure grip on slippery ice.*

Below left: *Youngsters play-fight on the floes.*

Below: *Increasing human activity in the Arctic attracts bears to scavenge on the inevitable waste.*

Above: *Time out for the bears to bask in the bright sunshine of the long Arctic summer days.*

Opposite: *Expert swimmers, polar bears may cruise the cold seas, feeding and floe-hopping over hundreds of kilometres.*

Right: *Cubs are tiny at birth but by the time they emerge from the den three months later, they weigh up to 10 kg. When weaned at two years of age they may tip the scales at around 180 kg.*

good at taking advantage of it when it is present. An adult bear can eat 10 per cent of its body weight in 30 minutes and the stomach of a large male can hold up to 70 kg of food! Polar bears are essentially opportunist hunters and will take walrus pups, beluga whales, bearded seals and even birds when they can. But by far the major part of their diet is comprised of a few species of seals and as seals weigh between 35 and 115 kg they provide a good meal at a sitting. The ringed seal is the most abundant marine mammal in the Arctic and is a favourite prey species, but periodic declines in its numbers, as well as weather conditions that make it difficult to hunt, can have devastating effects on polar bear populations.

Although seal die-offs do take their toll on bear numbers, it is increasing human activity in the Arctic which poses the greatest danger to the ice-bear. For despite the fact that populations are currently healthy, any increase in polar bear mortality would have disastrous effects because polar bears reproduce so slowly. In the past the remoteness of most polar bear habitat has made its conservation relatively easy. Now, however, northern oil, gas and mineral deposits are being discovered

period, polar bears find the winter months a good time for foraging and it is only pregnant females that tend to den at this time of year. Conversely, some polar bears, in the southern Hudson Bay area for example, face lean times during the summer when the ice melts and instead of denning-up they enter an equivalent state of dormancy called 'walking hibernation', where they become lethargic and may lose more than 1 kg of fat each day. While a black bear can only hibernate in autumn or winter, and may starve at other times of the year if deprived of food and water, a polar bear can enter the dormant stage at any time in response to food shortages. This is highly advantageous to an animal living where the food supply is so unpredictable.

Just as polar bears can deal with a lack of food they are also extremely

Above: *Clad in the warmest of coats and insulated by a thick layer of fat, a bear can nap in perfect comfort even out on the open ice.*

Below: *Safely behind bars, tourists look warily down on an inquisitive bear's sniffing snout.*

Tundra Buggy Tours

to feed on, but a prowling bear usually ends up dead — shot by nervous residents. Government and industry are cooperating to try to prevent such conflicts through advance planning efforts. Even seemingly benign activities, such as ecotourism around critical summer habitats can create problems unless they are very carefully controlled.

Still more serious threats could come from environmental contaminants and global warming. Persistent toxic chemicals that accumulate in the sea, such as polychlorinated biphenyls (PCBs), have the potential to affect the reproduction of both seals and bears. Scientists are now collecting samples from bears found throughout the region in order to monitor contamination. PCBs break down only slowly and become concentrated in the fat of animals high in the food-chain. As polar bears are at the top of the chain and store and metabolize large amounts of fat yearly they are affected most. Polar bears in Svalbard have PCB tissue levels of 32 parts per million (ppm) — 70 ppm has been shown to affect reproduction in seals. Biologists are trying to decide if the high levels correlate with low reproduction rates currently being observed in the Svalbard bears. Canadian and Alaskan bears have only one fifth to one tenth these PCB levels, but the widespread occurrence of PCBs is cause for concern.

Just as serious in the long term is the prospect of global warming. Experts predict that polar regions will first feel the effects. Even slight temperature increases

and exploited. For example, the Arctic National Wildlife Refuge in northern Alaska is potentially the most important oil and gas prospect in the USA, but it is also a major polar bear denning area. Even if the clear threats from industrial pollution and disturbance are put aside, greater contact between bears and humans may cause problems. Bears are attracted to settlements where they can find waste scraps

Left: *For as long as Western people have known about polar bears they have captured the imagination. Native polar people referred to them as 'the great wanderers' and believed they were people who only put on bear skins when they left their igloos.*

Overleaf: *In splendid isolation a male and female meet at sunset — but for how much longer?*

could seriously alter the entire sea and ice systems on which the bears depend. Unfortunately, though, current theories are inconclusive and by the time accurate predictions can be made, changes that could affect the bears may already have begun. Unusually warm weather in late 1990 resulted in hundreds of hungry polar bears and thousands of walruses becoming stranded on Wrangel Island awaiting the ice to creep down from the north. While this situation cannot be ascribed to global warming — relatively normal ice conditions returned in the following two autumns — it gives some idea of the chaotic predator-prey imbalances that might occur on a regular basis if the amount and extent of sea-ice decreases.

The research and management activities of polar bear biologists around the globe have so far contributed to a successful and progressive conservation programme. But the increasing fear among scientists is that the fate of the ice-bear may be tied to events beyond their control.

John Hechtel

Below: *Day beds made in the snow help insulate the bears from the worst of the Arctic weather.*

Environmental Issues

General awareness of the sensitivity of our planet to snowballing human impact has broadened considerably over the last few years. Even so, the catalogue of problems continues to grow. But there are some encouraging signs that destructive forces can be mitigated by public concern, and here we look at the causes and effects of those threats that are moving closer to touching us all.

Rainforests continue to be cut at an alarming rate. These forests help maintain the balance of the atmosphere — without them global warming could pose a serious threat to all life in the future — but the informed Western consumer can have a say in their survival. More and more oil finds its way into the sea, while deadly chemicals flushed from the land add to the toxic load, threatening wildlife and the native peoples who rely on it — but there are increasing signs of resistance to the activities that damage the environment.

At the same time, the world's few remaining unique wildlife havens are coming under pressure — places like the Everglades, the remote Falkland Islands, or the cavernous depths of Caribbean blue holes. It is to be hoped that the lessons to be learned from those highly competitive species that manage to thrive in the face of our depredations may teach us to take a more harmonious line to the wider benefit of the world and wildlife in the future.

Above: *The shifting sands of the Sahara and other deserts threaten to extend further if average global temperatures continue to rise.*

Above right: *Once thought too wild and remote for exploitation, even lands of the cold far north are now at risk from development.*

Right: *On the borderline. The sea is a highly capable recycling plant but we are stretching its capacity to the limit as we pour in ever more waste, effluent, oils and toxic chemicals.*

LAND OF THE DAMMED

For five thousand years the James Bay Cree of what is now northern Quebec have depended on fish to see them through the winter. During the long frozen months, when other game is scarce, these native Americans have survived on trout, salmon, whitefish and northern pike, split and smoke-dried earlier in the season, or fished fresh through ice holes. Now the Cree, and their Inuit neighbours, are having to change their ways.

Deadly methyl mercury is beginning to build up in the fish. The naturally present but normally insoluble mercury, concentrated in the rocks, is being transformed into soluble methyl mercury by the bacterial action of rotting vegetation. This vegetation, which was once

Below: *The LG1 generating plant, part of the James Bay I project, and (**bottom**) one of the many huge reservoirs and spillways.*

riverside forest growth, is rotting because it now lies under water, submerged by the massive reservoirs of one of the world's largest hydro-electric schemes, the James Bay Project of the state-owned Hydro-Quebec company. In the first part of this project, known as James Bay I, the waters of three rivers were diverted — the Eastmain, Opinaca and Caniapiscau — to turn the La Grande River into a super-torrent. Huge dams backed up the swollen waters of the La Grande and its tributaries, flooding 15,000 sq km of terrain to create the reservoirs for electricity generation.

Hydro-Quebec is reorganizing natural water dynamics on an immense scale. With its watershed massively enlarged, the La Grande river is now ten times its normal size in winter when water is released to feed peak energy demands. In 1984 water thundering through the opened sluices of one dam drowned 10,000 caribou migrating across land downstream.

The second part of the project, James Bay II, is now underway. If it is ever completed, the whole project will flood an area of forest and wetland almost the size of Belgium. The flooded vegetation will rot, and the bacteria will release more mercury from the bedrock, which will travel inexorably up the food-chains, from fish to sea mammals, birds and humans. The Cree and the Inuit have seen the pictures from the tragedy of Minamata in Japan, where coastal dwellers ate fish contaminated with methyl mercury from a chemical plant, and suffered a generation and more of miscarriages, severe brain damage and deformity. The floodlands have already disrupted and destroyed vast areas of the Cree's traditional hunting

Left: *Trees, drowned in the course of flooding the land to create vast reservoirs, rot down and help chemically convert naturally present mercury into highly toxic soluble methyl mercury. The generating plant supplied by this reservoir is the biggest underground power station in the world and can supply enough electricity to power a city of four million people.*

Below: *A plaque to the memory of the Cree's ancestors, who are now lying under the waters of the La Grande reservoirs. If the James Bay II projects proceed, today's Cree have even more to lose — not only their remaining land, but also their lifestyle and cultural identity.*

Above: *The James Bay projects threaten beavers by flooding river valleys. Their loss is also that of the Cree, who find fewer to trap — which limits the number of pelts they can exchange for currency.*

Opposite, top: *If the first phase of James Bay II proceeds, the spectacular Great Whale River will be dammed up and lost.*

Opposite, bottom: *The enforced leap from a traditional lifestyle to settlement-bound consumer has caused the Cree inevitable problems, as they attempt to straddle two quite different cultures.*

Right: *The feeding and breeding habits of beluga whales could be disturbed by the huge volumes of freshwater released from the hydro-electric dams into Hudson Bay.*

terrain, where they pursued the caribou, moose, geese and other game which sustained them outside the winter months. Now they cannot eat the fish. The only alternatives available are the tinned and packaged products of the settlement stores, built with the money that was supposed to compensate for the destruction of their culture.

James Bay is the southernmost arm of Hudson Bay. The wild rivers of northwestern Quebec pour down off the granite to join the salt waters of the bay's eastern side. To the Cree, it was a rich homeland which had been long ignored by the French-speaking urban populations as too remote for commercial exploitation. But now the raw water energy of the region is seen as a valuable resource to generate and sell hydro-electricity for domestic use, for the smelting industry and others, and for export to the energy-hungry cities of the USA's north east.

Quebec's Prime Minister, Robert Bourassa, began his first term of office in 1970, and immediately began to set the stage for the James Bay Project, calling it 'the key to the economic progress of Quebec.' The Cree's happy isolation ended in 1971 when the provincial government budgeted a $12 million start-up fund for the project. But no one consulted the Cree and Inuit, who first learned of the plans from a newspaper; teams of surveyors, followed by bulldozers and road gangs, simply began to invade.

In 1973 the Cree went to court to try to prevent the project. After many months of

wrangling they won a blocking injunction but it was overturned four days later by the Quebec Court of Appeal. Fuelled by fears that they would be dispossessed without compensation, and reeling under official pressure to force the project through, the Cree and Inuit, with three Inuit villages abstaining, joined Hydro-Quebec and the Federal Government in signing the James Bay and Northern Quebec Agreement in 1975. Apart from cash, the treaty awarded the Cree and Inuit 14,000 sq km of reserves, fishing and hunting rights over a further 156,000 sq km, and trapping rights over the whole project area.

The La Grande River scheme first came into commission in 1979, and was selling electricity to customers two years later. James Bay II has two planned phases. The first, known as the Great Whale Project, involves damming four rivers to create a reservoir area of 3400 sq km. The second phase, known as the NBR project, involves the damming of the Nottaway, Broadback and Rupert rivers in the south of the region, creating 6500 sq km of reservoirs. If it is ever completed, James Bay I and II will be capable of producing 27,000 megawatts of electricity from a total flooded area of well over 24,000 sq km.

Despite the Agreement, a new generation amongst the 12,000 Cree and 6000 Inuit are now fighting a hard battle, with the support of environmental groups, to stop the James Bay II projects; and the newly discovered mercury hazard is a strong argument in their favour. It was not until 1979, with the turbines beginning to turn, that links were

made between the artificial flooding and the release of methyl mercury. The Cree already suffered from greater than normal mercury levels due in some part to atmospheric fallout caused by the wood pulp and paper industries. Most Cree were known to have a mercury load greater than 6 milligrams per kilogram of hair, — the standard limit set by the World Health Organization. From 1985 onwards, Hydro-Quebec kept claiming that levels in fish had peaked, but the levels in fish have continued to rise. Before mercury was

known to be a problem, entire regional wildlife populations were being wiped out by flooding. The extensive flooded areas also cut across several migration routes used by caribou, and destroyed wetlands of marsh and seagrass used as feeding stopovers by birds migrating from the Arctic. Cree hunters have noticed that geese no longer recognize their old grazing sites, and are forced to keep on flying.

In the long term no one is sure what the effects on wildlife and humans might be as seasonal patterns of freeze and thaw are disrupted. The massive winter inflow of freshwater into the saline waters of James Bay is already affecting the seasonal interaction of the waters, and the effect will be multiplied if and when the Great Whale project comes on line. This in turn will radically affect the spring blooming of ice algae and phytoplankton which are the basis of much of the food-chain. An increase of freshwater entering James Bay in the winter will also lengthen the life of ice cover and disrupt the normal water currents. Changes on this scale could affect life at all levels.

For the Cree, the James Bay Project spells the end of an era. Today many Cree still work their traditional family hunting 'lines' — long strips of wilderness — but the schemes are cutting across the lines, and the 1975 Agreement denies the Cree the extensive lands necessary for the operation of their hunting system which leaves half the available land 'fallow' each year. Many younger Cree are resentful of the signing away of their traditional heritage, and without the continuity of the hunting and fishing seasons the old skills and knowledge could disappear in one or two generations. The Cree are among the last Native Americans to maintain a traditional culture based on hunting. Denied game and afraid to eat fish, the Cree diet has deteriorated very rapidly, to the point where the modern diseases of inappropriate diet are beginning to be seen. The enforced leap from hunter-gatherers to settlement-bound consumers has also brought with it the inevitable social problems in the form of crime, drunkenness and family breakdown. In some ways the 1975 Agreement has left the Cree and the Inuit with a foot in both worlds, but a stake in neither

Moreover, there are powerful forces ranged against the Cree's opposition to the project. Many Québécois would like independence from Canada, so they have embraced the project as a way of financing a break. Hydro-Quebec, for example, enticed lucrative investment in aluminium smelting with the bait of the lowest electricity prices in the world. Nonetheless, the Cree and the Inuit are working to combat Hydro-Quebec's propaganda and the reluctance of Canadian federal authorities to stir up the hornet's nest of Quebec nationalism. Perhaps the most significant source of outside help has come from an unexpected quarter — potential electricity customers. In 1992 Governor Mario Cuomo pulled New York out of a contract to buy power from James Bay II after environmentalists lobbied for lower power usage. A recession in aluminium smelting has also put contracts on hold and two USA universities decided to sell off Hydro-Quebec bonds to avoid involvement in a damaging project.

With a planned capacity that might be far beyond what is saleable, the James Bay II projects are in limbo at present, stymied by lack of customers, and under pressure from environmental groups and the Cree and the Inuit themselves, who are making a brave effort to save their traditional way of life before it is too late.

Duncan Brewer

Below & bottom: *Methyl mercury can accumulate in fish tissue to concentrations 100 million times the level in water. This problem may prevent the Cree from fishing for and eating fish in winter for at least a century.*

CONSERVING THE FALKLANDS

Opposite: Once hunted mercilessly for its oil, the rockhopper penguin is now a valued tourist attraction.

Below & bottom: The islands appear deceptively idyllic in the sunshine, but only low shrubs and tussock grass can withstand the searing westerly gales.

Four hundred and fifty kilometres to the east of Argentina's coastline lie the British dependent territories of the Falkland Islands. These low, windswept islands and the seas around them teem with a special kind of wildlife closely tied to the food-rich waters of the South Atlantic. There are huge numbers of breeding seabirds here, in particular, black-browed albatrosses, shearwaters and four species of penguin. Spectacular marine mammals such as the southern sea lion, elephant and fur seals all breed here too, and pods of whales and dolphins abound offshore. But where wildlife concentrates, people are seldom far away and these remote islands bear the many marks of human activity — from whaling to warfare — after nearly two and a half centuries of occupation.

As with so many remote islands, the influence of people and, equally important, their travelling menagerie of animals, has had serious implications for the unique and relatively specialized native wildlife. On East Falkland, domestic cattle, horses and pigs fared well on the islands' local tussock grass, but as the grass is very sensitive to being grazed it was soon driven to inaccessible rocky slopes adjacent to the seashore. The subsequent introduction of sheep saw the almost total destruction of tussock — a pattern that was repeated on West Falkland and almost all of the larger offshore islands.

The native fauna fared little better than the native flora. Hunting has played a major role in dramatically reducing bird and mammal populations on and around the islands. Elephant seals and fur seals were hunted almost to extinction for their oil and skins, and following their demise, hunters focused on sea lions until their numbers fell so low that their pursuit became unprofitable.

Penguins, particularly rockhoppers, have also been mercilessly hunted for oil. The first locally recorded penguin oil industry was started in 1862 in response to the scarcity of seals. One penguin yielded approximately half a litre of oil. This 'industry' peaked after only a year or so and lasted a mere 16 years in all — so great was the slaughter. Exactly how many birds died during this period will never be known, but it is estimated that at least one and a half to two million birds, mainly rockhoppers, probably perished.

The Falklands bird fauna is relatively specialized — due to the lack of trees all bird species have to nest on or close to the ground — but it is not restricted to seabirds. In total, 185 species have been recorded on the islands, of which 61 species breed. Of these species, only 18

Above: *The Falklands flightless steamer duck, or logger, is the only species of bird endemic to the islands. An ungainly and heavy inshore bird, it is also remarkably aggressive, and has even been known to kill other birds.*

Right: *Following a downpour, a rockhopper penguin takes a shower under an impromptu waterfall.*

are true landbirds; the majority of species are dependent upon a salt or freshwater environment. Several of the species are present in internationally important numbers. Estimates suggest that the Falklands are the most important breeding sites in the world for black-browed albatross, gentoo penguin, rockhopper penguin and thin-billed prion. There are also important populations of grey-backed storm-petrel, Antarctic skua, fairy prion and, possibly, the dolphin gull and king shag.

Most of the native mammals are marine species. In addition to seals and sea lions, the mammal which inspires particular awe is the killer whale, or orca. No large species of mammal occurs on the islands themselves, although many species have been introduced. One of the most enigmatic species present is the sea otter, as no one knows whether it was deliberately brought to the Falklands or not.

But what of the current threats to wildlife? During the last 25 years considerable progress has been made in offering the still plentiful wildlife further protection. The first major step towards nature conservation was the Nature Reserves Ordinance of 1964 which recognized

species of importance as well as the need to protect wildlife habitats. This legislation was aimed primarily at protecting the smaller tussock islands and was consolidated by the setting up of reserves after

Right: *Pods of killer whales patrol the shallow inshore waters, particularly when large numbers of penguins are breeding and seals and sea lions are pupping. There they prey on the unwary stragglers returning from fishing trips.*

the purchase of several islands and the acquisition of others by the Royal Society for Nature Conservation. Now there are at least 53 islands and islets which have been declared nature reserves.

In spite of the establishment of protected areas and the decline in hunting, today's wildlife faces renewed threats. Some of these threats are difficult to quantify but all may have a bearing on the future wildlife value of the islands. The recent expansion of the fisheries industry in the local fertile seas, for example, may have important implications for seabird and marine mammal populations. On the islands many of the larger farm settlements have been divided up and are now farmed as smaller units. This may leave smaller tussock islands open to private development and means that close cooperation between conservation groups and small farmers is essential to ensure that vulnerable breeding birds are protected. Additional threats may arise from the introduction of predators such as rats or cats to small islands. In some instances these two animals have been known to eradicate whole populations of island birds. Pollution poses another threat. In March 1992 a potentially serious incident occurred close to Beauchene Island, an island which holds almost half a million pairs of black-browed albatrosses and rockhopper penguins. The sinking of the trawler, *Lord Shackleton II* resulted in an oil spill from a ruptured fuel tank, and the heaviest concentrations of oil occurred in the vicinity of the seabird colonies. Though the slick dispersed naturally after several days, the long-term effects have

yet to be seen. Moreover, it was thought that the wreckage which washed up on the island may have carried rats ashore. In response, Falklands Conservation — the islands' leading conservation organization — laid poison baits to ensure that any rats that had arrived ashore did not survive to threaten breeding bird populations.

Three pieces of legislation already provide a degree of protection for Falklands wildlife. The Wild Animals and Birds Protection Ordinance gives general protection to most species, although game and a small number of 'pest' species are excluded. A Nature Reserves Ordinance allows for the establishment and protection of nature reserves; entry into such reserves is restricted and activities such as the cutting and burning of the vegetation is prohibited. And the Seal Fishery Ordinance of 1881 still provides protection for a number of Seal Reserves.

In addition to legislation, the successful establishment of the charitable organization Falklands Conservation has been vital in helping to monitor seabird and marine mammal populations around the islands, and in ensuring that any ongoing and development legislation meets all the requirements laid down to protect the islands' wildlife.

It is to be hoped that the increasing interest in the wildlife of the South Atlantic, inspired by the more readily available opportunities for people to visit the Falklands, will encourage the conservation of some of the most spectacular wildlife in the world for generations to come.

Tony Stones

Above: *The sea otter is essentially a marine species which lives amongst dense beds of coastal kelp around remote tussock islands. Present in very low numbers, sightings of this creature always arouse much local interest.*

LOSING THE WOODS FOR THE TREES

Opposite: *Fires can add massively to the destruction of rainforest wrought by man — as in Borneo in 1983, when fire destroyed over 40,000 sq km of lowland rainforest.*

Below: *Sarawak is the world's largest source of unprocessed timber. Between 1962 and 1985 30 per cent of Sarawak's forests were logged and at the present rate all of its rainforest will be gone by the end of the decade.*

Our planet is losing nearly 400,000 square metres of tropical rainforest a minute. This destruction is occurring not just in the forests of South America, which have been the major focus of media attention, but also in the rainforests of Africa and Asia. It is now estimated that nearly 200,000 sq km of rainforest are being destroyed worldwide each year. If this rate of destruction continues, then there will be no rainforest left by the year 2035.

Tropical rainforests are the richest of all plant communities and are among the oldest ecosystems on the planet. These ecosystems are vitally important not only for the wealth of plant and animal life they support but also because they play a fundamental role in the maintenance of the planet's carbon balance. By absorbing carbon dioxide, rainforests recycle carbon, which is the building block of all life.

Rainforests also provide a way of life for indigenous tribes and yield plant chemicals from which drugs used to treat serious diseases, including AIDS, can be made.

In 1990 it was estimated that in Latin America, 76,300 sq km of tropical rainforest are lost each year, in Africa this figure is roughly 16,000 sq km, similar to the rate of loss in Asia. In South-east Asia 25,000 sq km are thought to be destroyed each year. In the context of the original area of forest cover, these figures are alarming. For example, in São Paulo state in Brazil, forest cover has dropped in 120 years from 80 per cent to 8 per cent; by 2000 it is expected to occupy only 3 per cent.

Threats to the rainforest are legion. Agriculture is one; others include the burning of vast areas for cattle grazing to meet the huge demand for cheap beef, and clearance for open cast mineral mining. Urban and industrial expansion threaten the forests too. This is necessary in the poorer developing countries, but development is often funded by the sale of rainforest timber and in 1994, logging of the rainforest poses one of the most serious threats to its survival.

In Japan, the USA and many European countries the demand for quality hardwood timber, particularly mahogany, teak and rosewood, remains high. As a result, these hardwoods command enormous prices on the world market and provide a vital source of income for developing countries. It is all too easy for loggers to purchase huge tracts of land, known as concessions, and then rapidly strip them

Below: *Newly logged areas are commonly converted to plantations to grow speedily marketable crops like oil palm.*

Below: *In the first 65 years of this century about half of all rainforest in the developing world was cleared for agriculture or grazing for cheap beef.*

of all the trees, before moving their bulldozers and chainsaws on to another new concession and repeating the process.

Today, the fastest destruction of rainforest is probably occurring in Sabah and Sarawak, the two states which make up East Malaysia on the island of Borneo. In 1987, the botanical journal *Flora Malesiana Bulletin* reported 'The facts are that within another five years or so the lowland forests of Sabah will have been logged'. It may be tempting to temper such prospects with the fact that rainforests do regenerate, and it is possible to maintain the forests to give a controlled supply of timber for the foreseeable future. But this concept of sustainability is largely ignored by governments and modern loggers.

Logging in the 20th century is highly destructive. Using bulldozers to barge access paths to the most valuable trees which are then cut haphazardly means that 10 trees can be lost for every one felled. Furthermore, the rainforest is very rarely left to recover. In some cases the logged areas are immediately converted to plantations. Even if logged forest is left for a while, economic pressures and the demands of increasing populations often mean that the regenerating areas are logged again before they have recovered fully. When this happens the forest soil becomes exhausted and incapable of supporting even secondary forest and then such areas are abandoned as wasteland.

The fundamental conflict between the producers in the developing world and consumers in the West is illustrated by the plight of the International Tropical Timber Agreement (ITTA). This was signed in 1983 by the 41 countries of the International Tropical Timber Organization (ITTO). There were great hopes for the ITTA as it was the first initiative to establish a system of consultation and cooperation between the major producer and consumer countries. Furthermore, conservation was at the top of the agenda. However, since the agreement was signed, a quarter of the remaining tropical rainforest has been lost. November 1992 saw the beginning of the renegotiation of the ITTA, a process which could go on indefinitely, as most of the members have become disillusioned. The

SUSTAINABILITY

Sustainability is defined as 'the maintenance of a forest to yield a continuing and non-declining flow of benefits and products'. This means ensuring that natural regeneration from pioneer to climax tree species occurs. Climax species are the dominant hardwoods whose timber is the most valuable. Pioneer species are soft-wooded, fast-growing and short-lived opportunists, able to colonize gaps quickly, creating secondary forest and providing suitable conditions for the growth of climax species. However, this regeneration is slow; it takes at least 120 years for an entire rainforest to renew itself.

Sustainability therefore involves selective cutting so that only a few large trees are removed and enough medium-sized trees are left untouched so that after, say, 30 years there will be a new crop of trees to harvest.

tropical timber producing nations, such as Malaysia, Indonesia and Brazil, are angry that the ITTO has never seriously addressed the subject of timber prices, terms of trade and market access — which could help them expand their sales worldwide; while many of the consuming nations are angry at the ITTO's inability to make the producers guarantee progress towards sustainable management. The timber producers also argue that Target 2000 (the ITTO's commitment to sustainable trade by 2000) should also apply to non tropical timber producers, insisting that the ITTA should become the International Timber Agreement (ITA).

Despite the political wrangling there have recently been global initiatives which do give some hope. Many of these rest on the realization of the rich nations that empty rhetoric is not enough, but that economic aid to the poorer nations is essential if the world's rainforests are going to be saved.

At the 1992 Earth Summit, in Rio, western nations agreed that the cost of achieving benefits associated with forest conservation requires increased international cooperation and should be equally shared by all. This may mean that developing

Left: *Tin ore extraction in Amazonia has damaged vast tracts of rainforest.*

Below: *High demand for hardwoods in the West encourages wasteful logging.*

Above: *The rapid expansion of the urban jungle, as here in Brazil, is often at the expense of rainforest.*

Right: *New roads slicing through the landscape funnel migrants deep into the rainforest and encourage further tree clearing along the way by farmers hungry for new land. Here, the BR364 highway cuts through the Brazilian forests.*

Below right & below: *In some newly logged areas forest regeneration is given a helping hand by 'enrichment planting' with hardwood seedlings. These are raised outside the forest, under schemes often financed by Western nations, before being planted out.*

Some organizations, particularly the International Union for the Conservation of Nature (IUCN), have provided enlightened investment and helped establish a network of globally important 'super parks', known as World Heritage Sites. Since the early 1970s over 3000 national parks have been created in all parts of the world's tropical rainforest with a total area of 4 million sq km — nearly half the land area of the entire USA. This means that at least some primary rainforest will remain untouched. Conservation areas also promote ecotourism, providing money for further protection of the forest. The introduction of Debt Swaps in the late 1980s by non-governmental organizations (NGOs), is another step towards the conservation of the forest. An NGO purchases part of a nation's debt from the lender and in exchange the nation sets aside areas for conservation.

Careful land planning is also fundamental to the conservation of the rainforests. Plantations may not be all bad news — they could provide an alternative supply of timber, thus relieving pressures to log primary forest. Further hope lies in the improvement of logging practices as embodied in the concept of Reduced Impact Logging (RIL). RIL means adopting practices such as creeper cutting; often creepers attached to a tree being logged also cling to other trees which are then also pulled down — this would result in massive reductions in forest damage. RIL also looks at ways of minimizing damage to the forest floor. In Sarawak such planning has reduced open logged spaces by 23 per cent in some areas. Many RIL schemes are financed by companies from richer nations; an agreement was signed in June 1992 between New England Power (NEP) from the USA and the Sabah Foundation, the organization responsible for logging concessions in Sabah. By this,

nations are given economic incentives to control logging more carefully. The same conference also saw the ratification of the Biodiversity Treaty. By this deal, Western countries gain access to biological resources, such as chemicals from plants, in return for money and assistance for the sustainable use of forests.

NEP have agreed to fund the adoption of RIL in this densely forested area with the ultimate aim of reducing tree loss and achieving sustainable logging.

However, all these positive initiatives may be meaningless unless there is tougher legislation on tropical timber imports. Ideally, developed nations should import only timber which has been logged sustainably. Already the Netherlands has stated that, after 1995, imports of tropical timber will be permitted only from sustainable sources. Switzerland has made a similar commitment, and Austria has just passed legislation to restrict tropical timber imports. The Forest Stewardship Council aims to establish a workable certification and labelling scheme for timber from well managed forests so that consumers can play their part in saving rainforest trees. And if consumers push for a higher profile, almost anything can be achieved. Action, like supporting environmental organizations, or avoiding buying

tropical woods that are not from sustainable sources, are steps we can all take. But there's an awful long way to go — less than 0.1 per cent of the world's rainforest is under any form of sustainable logging.

Dr Sally Uren

Above: *Logging robs indigenous peoples, like the Borneo/Sarawak Penan hunter-gatherers, of both their home and livelihood.*

RAINFOREST SPECIES LOSS

Logging disturbs rainforest animals in many ways: noise and activity may frighten them away from the area; birds and mammals such as hornbills, monkeys and deer may be hunted for food; while commercially valuable species, such as orang-utans, may be poached for the pet trade. The major threat, though, is from the destruction of habitat. Specialized species, which often occur in low densities, are very sensitive to this and may become locally extinct. Such sensitive species include Gurney's pitta, the green broadbill and the white-necked picathartes from West Africa — which will only nest on the sides of house-sized boulders by streams in deep forest. Other rainforest birds, such as hornbills, nest in holes in large trees. Such trees are rare in logged forests and as a result, the hornbills are even rarer.

Hornbills and other creatures are also important in moving seeds from place to place. Unless the seeds pass through their guts they will not germinate.

Without such species natural growth and regeneration are halted or slowed. Logging also leads to the fragmentation of the forest. Patches which remain are often too small to support predators — like forest eagles or cats. Even populations of small, common species may also die out if the forest fragments cannot support a year-round food supply or adequate den and nesting sites.

Above: *At risk: the rhinoceros hornbill and Brazilian tapir.*

TROUBLED WATERS

1993 began badly around the coasts of the world. Oil was still washing up on 100 km of the northern Spanish coastline, following an accident in December 1992 in which an oil tanker, the *Aegean Sea*, ran aground as it approached the port of La Coruña, bursting into flames and spilling its cargo. Then, on 5th January, another tanker, the *Braer*, struck Shetland off northern Scotland, and the world's television screens were filled with pictures of oil-smothered seabirds and waves turned black by the choking crude oil. Just 16 days later another tanker, the *Maersk Navigator*, caught fire and released its cargo of oil, following a collision with an empty tanker in the Strait of Malacca between Sumatra and Malaya.

As a result of these three accidents, within six weeks over 3 million barrels of crude oil were released into the sea. The total weight of this black cargo was about 380,000 tonnes, yet it is a measure of the amount of oil transported by sea that this would supply a large refinery for only about nine days. But perhaps the most disturbing statistic is that spills like these are just the tip of a particularly dark and oily iceberg, for every year well over 3 million tonnes of oil are spilled into the sea, and only an eighth of this comes from tanker accidents. Almost all the rest comes from routine spillages from tankers, industry and municipal wastes. But it is tanker accidents that best highlight the potential problems of allowing massive amounts of oil to contaminate our seas by concentrating attention on the ensuing scenes of local devastation.

The increase in the frequency of oil accidents in recent years is a direct product of the world-wide recession, which is driving oil companies to run tankers beyond their designed life of around 15 years — the *Aegean Sea* was 19 years old and the *Braer* 18. Increasingly too, oil companies are cutting overheads by using less skilled, multinational crews, and captains are being tempted to take risky short-cuts to reduce travel time and cost.

But what effect does this oil have on the wildlife living in the stricken area? In the case of the *Maersk Navigator* we may never know, because there were no experts on hand to report the damage. But within a few days, an oil slick 560 km long had drifted to within 16 km of the

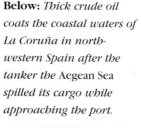

Below: *Thick crude oil coats the coastal waters of La Coruña in north-western Spain after the tanker the* Aegean Sea *spilled its cargo while approaching the port.*

Indian island of Great Nicobar. The living coral reefs of its southern coast are particularly susceptible to damage by oil, and the area is also important for turtles and dugongs — the gentle, plant-eating sea mammals also known as sea-cows.

The immediate after-effects of the *Aegean Sea* oil spill are better documented. It was estimated that around a third of all the gulls and cormorants in the bay off La Coruña had been affected by the oil. Among the few birds rescued and treated for oil contamination were several of the rare Iberian race of the common guillemot, of which fewer than 100 birds remained before the spill.

Serious damage also occurred beneath the sea surface. Up to 10,000 tonnes of shellfish were reported to have been killed by the oil, and it was estimated that it would take 20 years for the local fishery to recover.

Ironically, the *Aegean Sea* was carrying North Sea oil from a major oil terminal at Sullom Voe on Shetland, where a major spill had been feared for years. As it happened, the oil that was to pollute Shetland was not the island's own. The *Braer* was carrying 84,000 tonnes of Norwegian light crude to Canada, but mischance, engine failure, and the worst storms in

Above: *The* Braer *lies wrecked near Quendale Bay, Shetland, 1993.*

Below: *Kuwati oil well alight and spewing oil into the Persian Gulf.*

Below: *Oil in the sea means oil in the food-chain of the great northern diver, harlequin duck, dugong and common seal.*

A DEADLY DOUSING

Oil kills seabirds and coastal mammals, such as otters, by clogging their feathers and fur, leading to loss of insulation and death by hypothermia. Oiled birds also lose buoyancy and can die of exhaustion or drowning. Oiled animals try to clean themselves by grooming, but the oil they ingest can be fatal, or can seriously affect their breeding capacity.

Seabirds may be particularly susceptible because an oily sheen on the water surface is normally a sign of fish beneath, tempting them to dive

Above: *Oil mats the fur of a sea otter.*

Above: *A tragic end for an oiled cormorant.*

straight into oil slicks.

Whales, dolphins and seals, which have a thick insulating layer of blubber rather than fur to keep them warm, are less affected by oil on their bodies, but are particularly at risk from the toxic fumes which they inhale at the water's surface.

Above: *Oil-poisoned trout.*

Shetland for 100 years led to her cargo being dumped on the southern coast — one of the most important areas for seabirds in north-western Europe.

The world's press descended on Shetland to report on what was predicted to be a major ecological tragedy. With the *Braer* slowly breaking up in ferocious seas and steadily leaking oil, reports sent around the world showed how winds up to hurricane force were hampering efforts to salvage

the remaining cargo and to clean up the developing oil slick.

However, the expected picture of wildlife casualties never materialized. Instead, the tempestuous seas rapidly broke up and dispersed the oil slick, ensuring that most of Shetland's coastline was left free from a visible blanket of oil. Within ten days of the accident the emergency was declared over, the reporters went home, and Shetland was said to have had a 'lucky escape'.

The consequences for local people were devastating, however. Farmed salmon, valued at £8-£10 million, had to be destroyed because of oil contamination, fisherman were banned from fishing over a large area at risk from pollution, and crops near the wreck-site were damaged by wind-blown oil. There was concern for human health, too. High concentrations of volatile components from the oil, which readily vaporize, hung in the air. Some of these are known to be cancer-causing.

But did Shetland have a lucky escape? The ecological effects can be difficult to assess fully as the results are often slow to appear. Some creatures, for example, may not die until many days later, perhaps far from the spill site, and only the most serious and immediate victims close to the scene are likely to be noted. The storms which broke up the oil slick must also have carried many oiled birds out to sea, so that the casualties counted on the beaches may have been only a small proportion of those that died. Even so, over 1500 birds were reported dead within three weeks of the accident and among them were 850 shags and over 200 black guillemots: scientists fear that the final death-toll for these species could reach 1 per cent of the world population. The oil also killed at least 96 long-tailed ducks and 13 great northern divers, species which are far from common around

European coastlines. Because the oil was light grade and dispersed rapidly in the storms, seals and otters were less badly affected — at least initially.

The storms may have been a saving grace in another way: by preventing the widespread application of chemical dispersants onto the oil slick. In the past, such dispersants have been shown to do more harm than the oil itself: the devastating effects of the dispersants used in cleaning up after the *Torrey Canyon* tanker accident in Cornwall in 1967 are still detectable by marine biologists 27 years later. Dispersants do not remove the oil. Instead, they spread it more widely through the marine environment, adding their own chemical load to a system already overloaded with oil. Carefully used, they can help to reduce immediate damage to important bird populations and to keep oil off coastlines, but even modern dispersants are still a cause for concern.

Floating booms to keep oil away from sensitive areas, skimmers to scoop oil from the surface, or swift action to pump oil from a stricken tanker before it breaks up are far safer ways to reduce the impact of a spill — but all proved impracticable in the conditions around Shetland.

Despite the dispersing effect of the storms, dead fish began to be washed up

Above, top & left: *Seabird colonies, farmed salmon, and reefs are all at risk from the deadly effects of oil pollution.*

Above & top: *Dispersants break up slicks quickly but add their own toxic load to the sea. Skimming and scooping by hand is slower, harder work, but a far safer way to deal with a spill when weather permits.*

Shetland, Spain, Sumatra or wherever else there were oil spills in 1993. In March 1989, the *Exxon Valdez* ran aground in Prince William Sound, Alaska, spilling 38,000 tonnes of oil. Although conditions were perfect for clean-up work, the oil company was initially slow to respond, allowing the oil to spread along 1500 km of pristine coastline. 980 sea otters, 146 bald eagles and some 33,000 seabirds are known to have died soon after the spill. The company later spent $1.3 billion on its clean-up efforts, but these were largely ineffective. Attempts to remove beached oil by high pressure steam merely cooked the animals on the shoreline; even by 1993, only 200 km of the beaches affected were fit for animal life.

Long-term effects may prove even more serious. Fish that hatched in the area during the summer of 1989 had withered muscles, fin deformities, misshapen spines, damaged jaws or even no jaws at all. The death rate of salmon eggs in polluted areas is still much higher than

soon after the *Braer* hit the rocks, and many were deeper-water species, suggesting that the toxic components of the oily brew were already being carried well below the surface. Within a few days, scuba divers reported dead shellfish, worms, crabs, winkles and starfish on the seabed near the wreck — perhaps the first signs of more pervasive damage.

The effects on the fish that spawn around Shetland are impossible to assess. These are the main food for the islands' internationally important seabird colonies, and their eggs and young are much more sensitive to chemical damage than the adults. A serious risk also remains that toxins released from the oil may have been taken in by the tiny plants and animals of the marine plankton, and will be passed up the food-chain, affecting all marine life in the area for many years to come.

Two earlier disasters emphasize that there are no grounds for complacency in

normal, leading to concern for the future salmon population. Other effects are only now being reported by scientists. Seals have suffered brain damage similar to that caused by solvent abuse in humans, leaving the animals disorientated. As a result, many probably drowned unnoticed and there are one-third fewer seals in the area than before the accident. The same toxic effect may account for the mysterious disappearance of many of the area's killer whales. An unusually high death rate is also being noted in adult sea otters in the area. Harlequin ducks have failed to breed since the accident, probably because of oil toxins in the mussels they eat. Some seabird colonies have also failed to recover from the huge loss of breeding adults killed by the oil spill.

Early suggestions of recovery after Saddam Hussein's 'ecoterrorism' in 1991, when oil was deliberately released into the Persian Gulf, are proving to be premature. Although thousands of seabirds were immediate casualties, a far more insidious

effect of the oil is now becoming evident. In 1993, tens of thousands of white-cheeked terns in the north of the Gulf abandoned their eggs. Other species of tern turned cannibal and ate the few chicks that did hatch. The cause was a desperate shortage of fish, most probably resulting from the effects of the oil on breeding fish after the spill, and from the destruction of plankton by the oil, which is now being released slowly from the seabed.

Whether the long term effects of the 1993 oilspills will prove to be as bad as those from the Gulf War or the *Exxon Valdez* remains to be seen. But it is certainly wrong — and dangerously complacent — to suggest, as one British journalist did, that 'the one thing we know about oil spills is that the ecosystem bounces back remarkably quickly'. Nothing could be further from the truth. Oil may seem to disappear in the sea but its polluting effects may not remain hidden for ever.

Michael Scott

Top: *Rescue city: a sea otter rescue unit working in the aftermath of the Exxon Valdez spill in Alaska, 1989.*

Above: *Hay-backed booms strung across the mouths of creeks help stop oil from the sea washing into salt marsh systems inland.*

Left: *Flushing oil from Alaskan beaches in 1989. Five years on, only 200 km of 1500 km of affected coast is back to normal.*

UNFAIR COMPETITION

Opposite: *The Yukon is centre-stage in the battle between humans and wolves over the 'right' to hunt caribou.*

Below: *Competition between the European wolf and livestock farming interests have been largely responsible for the eradication of this creature across much of its range. Even now, the few wolves that stray from Russian forests into stockraising areas of Scandinavia are shown no mercy.*

At the beginning of 1993 the territorial government of the Yukon, in northwest Canada, announced a plan to destroy three-quarters of the wolf population in a 20,000 sq km region known as the Aishihik Lake area. Some 150 of the estimated total of 200 wolves were to be shot from helicopters in what was described as a 'careful, temporary reduction in wolf numbers'. According to the plan another 50 wolves were to be shot the following year, and a further 50 each year thereafter.

Officially, this exercise was promoted as a 'caribou herd recovery program', designed to arrest an apparent — but unproven — decline in local caribou numbers. As wolves kill caribou, logic suggested that if there were fewer caribou then wolves must be the culprits. But this conclusion ignored the facts that wolves and caribou have co-existed in this area for thousands of years without problems, and that the apparent decline in the caribou population coincided with a marked increase in human activity in the area. It also followed a period of particularly intense caribou hunting by humans. Indeed, it was human hunters who first reported the lack of caribou.

Wildlife groups opposed the wolf cull, accused the government of stupidity and proposed a variety of alternative measures designed to keep humans, and particularly hunters, out of the Yukon altogether. The end of the story is yet to be told, but the essential facts of the case are inescapable: when two species find themselves in competition, and one of them is ours, we will usually win — if we want to.

Over the millennia we have proved to be the planet's most powerful species, but the brain-power that has helped us achieve this position has rarely been applied sensitively to the creatures we compete with. All too often, the losers are eradicated or driven to the brink of extinction before their plight is noticed. But we are not quite so all-conquering as we often like to believe. Our frustration in failing to compete and win against some species is signally exposed in our arrogant labelling of them as 'pests'. Perhaps fortunately for us, the fortitude and tenacity of such creatures, as they resist our best efforts to win at all costs, will teach us how better to live along with, not without, the wildlife of the planet.

As erstwhile hunter-gatherers, we have always been in competition with other species with similar tastes. Long ago the competition was probably more equal, with people having to fight hard for their space and for a place at the table among

bigger, stronger rivals. But the feud probably started in earnest when we left the open marketplace of the hunting and gathering grounds and began raising animals and crops for food. Inevitably, this attracted direct competition with predators. Rearing animals, however, encourages the farmer to regard them as property, so any predator that carries them off is not only a rival, but a thief. And while a big stick may be adequate to drive off even a strong predator, the development of efficient weapons enabled the farmer to make sure it never came back. As a result most of the big predators have been eradicated from the developed world.

One of the biggest of all predators, the lion, was forced from its former haunts in Europe over 2000 years ago. The European wolf fared better, and was still relatively common in the early medieval period: it is recorded that the bodies of the defeated at the Battle of Hastings in 1066 were left to be devoured by the wolves. But today the wolf is virtually extinct throughout most of Western Europe almost entirely as a result of persecution by farming interests.

Much the same fate has overtaken a variety of smaller predators which are also regarded as

Below: *Sheep ranchers in Montana hunt the coyote from the air in order to protect their huge flocks.*

Top: *Competitive predators like mink fall foul of fishermen and fish farmers alike.*

Above: *Weasels, like this short-tail, are trapped and poisoned because they threaten valuable gamebirds, chickens and their eggs.*

Right: *We have a special name for creatures, such as the rabbit, that defeat all our attempts to control them — pests.*

damage nets. Even fish-eating birds have not escaped attention. The red-breasted merganser, a fish-eating duck, has been blamed for the dwindling numbers of salmon and trout in many European rivers, and persecuted as a result. Falling fish stocks are more likely to be due to overfishing and pollution, but the lack of fish has made impoverished fishermen see all other fish-eaters as threats to their livelihoods. In reality, however, our taste for fish has actually destroyed or threatened the existence of many of our fish-eating rivals because we have fished many waters bare.

Predators are our most obvious direct competitors for food and space but, almost without exception, they have been either exterminated or marginalized. Consequently, their rivalry is negligible compared to that of the nibbling hordes of plant-eaters and omnivores which have become both direct and indirect competitors. Many of these creatures have foiled our attempts to confine them — in fact, they present altogether stiffer competition.

Consider the European rabbit. Originally restricted to the Spanish peninsula, it was probably one of the prey species for which we competed along with our predatory rivals, the fox, lynx and wolf. Then we domesticated it and transported it throughout Europe, where it ultimately went native. Even so, as a grass-eater, it did not threaten us directly. The northern winters and accompanying food shortages kept

competitors by farmers and game breeders alike. Animals such as coyotes, foxes, wild cats, mink, stoats and weasels are regularly shot, trapped or poisoned, often in defiance of conservation laws, because they kill or threaten domestic sheep, hens, rabbits or gamebirds. Birds of prey, such as eagles, suffer likewise: in North America the bald eagle, the national symbol of the USA, is still widely persecuted and has become a rarity in the eastern states. In Finland up to 8000 goshawks are killed each year by hunters intent on protecting hand-reared pheasant chicks.

Similar conflicts arise in the sea, despite the fact that the harvest of the sea is in no sense the 'property' of those who seek it, any more than the caribou of the Yukon belong to Canadian hunters. Seals, in particular, are regarded as a threat to fish stocks, notably in the North Atlantic where the grey seal has been subjected to regular culling in response to the fishing industry's claims that they reduce catches and the rabbit in check and, in general, it retained its status as a welcome prey animal. But in the 18th and 19th centuries new agricultural methods enabled farmers to grow crops throughout the winter, and this presented the rabbit with a guaranteed supply of young plant shoots to feed on during the months when its primary food, grass, was not growing. The result was a massive increase in the rabbit population which wrought havoc on crops. From simple prey, the rabbit had become a competitor and a pest.

The rabbit's impact in New Zealand was even more serious. Released there by English sheep-raising colonists, the rabbit found itself with abundant food and no

predators. Inevitably the population grew unchecked, to the point where rabbits began to overrun the sheep pastures. Intense competition with the sheep followed, and because rabbits can graze closer to the ground than sheep, the rabbits won. The fate of the Mount Nicholas station in Otago, South Island, was typical: before rabbits became established in 1864, 20,000 sheep grazed 300 sq km of mountain pasture. Twenty years later the same land was feeding a mere 2000 sheep — and about a million rabbits. The rabbit plague here and elsewhere was eventually brought under partial control, but the animal is still regarded as a serious pest.

Similar conflicts have arisen worldwide between domestic livestock and indigenous grazers. The American bison was virtually exterminated in the 19th century — along with the native American peoples who relied on it — because it grazed

Top: *Grey seals are culled because it is claimed they reduce fish stocks.*

Above: *The bald eagle is persecuted for taking salmon, yet its catches have no impact on fish numbers.*

Above *Red-breasted mergansers, fish-eating sawbill ducks, are often seen as unwelcome visitors, especially on game-fish rivers and lakes.*

Below: *Where large rival predators, like the bobcat, still thrive they have usually been driven into marginal areas by human persecution. Even then they may be pursued if they possess a valuable pelt.*

land that could be exploited by the more valuable domestic cattle. The scimitar-horned oryx has been eradicated from the arid regions of North Africa largely for the same reason. On the other hand, elsewhere in Africa, wild antelopes have proved so competitive, because of their suitability to their native environment, that they have been domesticated and are reared in place of cattle.

Pasture competition is a serious problem for ranchers, but farmers are more concerned with animals that eat their crops. Some of the most damaging are the great swarms and flocks of animals that descend from the skies to plunder a field and move on. The red-billed quelea, for example, an African member of the weaver family, flies in dense clouds of up to a million birds that swirl down on to fields of grain and strip them bare, causing

crop damage estimated at around $22 million each year. Yet despite the fact that pest controllers have used dynamite, petrol bombs, flame-throwers and poison to kill up to 180 million birds annually, the quelea remains a major pest throughout Africa south of the Sahara.

Less spectacular, but more insidious, are the armies of insects that swarm over crops throughout the world: insects such as the potato-munching colorado beetle and the sap-sucking aphids. Such creatures have become pests because they can multiply at prodigious rates in ideal conditions, conditions which, ironically, we have created by growing their food-plants in vast concentrations. Their rate of reproduction also outpaces our attempts to control them, not simply by pressure of numbers, but because a fast turnover of generations encourages a rapid rate of adaptation to chemical pesticides as vulnerable strains are killed off and resistant strains flourish to take their place.

solution to the problem of birds colliding with aircraft, particularly jet aircraft. Such collisions are invariably fatal for the birds, but they can also put the machine, the crew and passengers in jeopardy. Sucked through a jet engine at high speed, bird remains can smash the fan-blades and occasionally cause engine failure. Some airport authorities have become so worried about this problem that they employ falconers and bird-scaring devices to clear the skies near runways.

Airspace may be precious around an airport, but for most people, in this era of accelerating population growth, the most important space is land area. In this respect nearly all animals have become our competitors. Increasingly, our activities reveal that we should not approach competition with other species on a win-at-all-costs basis. For by pushing other creatures out of their own environment, or trying to crush them mindlessly underfoot, we will not only impoverish the world but also ourselves.

John Woodward

Left & bottom: *The natural world fights back with uncontrollable invasions of species, such as the red-billed quelea and sap-sucking aphids.*

Below: *Exploiting its new-found protection, the long-eared bat has come back to roost in many a home's roofspace.*

Several animals are seen as competitors despite having no designs on our food supply. A simple example is the humble furniture beetle, or woodworm — an insect that, in nature, bores through dead timber. When we adopted wood as a building material we adopted the woodworm as well, and vast sums are now spent each year on chemicals to keep the beast at bay. Even greater damage is done by the wood-boring termites of the tropics, where many occupiers of wooden houses have to battle non-stop to prevent their homes becoming meals for termites.

Other domestic competitors include the bats that may take up residence in the lofts of our houses — their response to our eradication of their natural roosting sites. But while bats can now compete with us for roofspace, thanks to their new-found legal protection, birds often suffer badly in competition for their own element — airspace. Aero-engineers throughout the world have yet to find a

BLUE HOLES OF THE BAHAMAS

Under the seabed lies a world within a world in the shape of vast submerged caverns linked by dark passages which have been hollowed out of solid rock by the unceasing action of water over hundreds of thousands of years. Such caverns occur in a number of places, notably in the Caribbean, but nowhere are they more spectacular or widespread than in the islands of the Bahamas. Here, in the warm, clear waters of the shallow seas, the circular entrance shafts to some of the cave networks plunge so deep that they show up from the air as deep blue holes in the seabed.

Caribbean legend tells that blue holes are the lairs of the 'Lusca', a boat-eating sea-monster, but though this fabled beast has so far given science the slip, the caves are actually home to a fascinating array of marine creatures, including sponges, corals, fan-worms and a number of specially adapted cave-dwellers — as well as a unique order of crustaceans.

Speleologists — divers, potholers and scientists who explore and study cave systems — have been fascinated by blue holes since they were first investigated in the 1950s. The Canadian diver, George Benjamin, was among the first to lead survey teams into several of the cave systems and he discovered some spectacular grottoes. But many systems

Right: *Amongst the planet's last secret places, blue holes — submerged cave systems — may yet reveal new surprises within their spectacular labyrinthine galleries.*

Below: *Entrance shafts to blue holes, here inland, show up from the air as dark patches in the water.*

Above: *Under artificial light, magnificent speleothems — stalactites and stalagmites — emerge from the gloom to create a ghostly white architectural fantasy.*

plunge to depths that were beyond the limitations of the diving equipment of the day, and Benjamin could not explore them fully. Since then, technological advances have brought some of the blue holes' secrets to light, but many more still remain to be discovered.

The Bahamas' name comes from the Spanish *baja mar*, meaning shallow sea, and the islands are local high points of an underlying limestone base, 8 km thick,

formed by the deposition of sea-borne sediment spanning 100 million years. It is within these rocks that the secret of the blue holes' formation lies.

Rain, percolating through the highly porous limestone, collects under the islands to form aquifers — lens-shaped stores of freshwater which 'float' within the rock on top of the denser salt water which seeps in from the surrounding sea. The interface where salt and freshwater

shape the cave systems. During the last ice age, for example, the sea dropped to about 120 m below its current level, stranding some of the caverns above the water line. Magnificent white speleothems — stalactites and stalagmites — were then formed in the dry caves by limestone-enriched rainwater dripping though the roofs. Some of these grew into grand pillars, others were left as thin and delicate as straws. The water also found its way downwards, following natural fault lines in the rock, to create vertical linking shafts between galleries at different levels. Later, when the ice retreated and the sea rose, these subterranean grottoes were drowned again. In fact, some caverns have probably been exposed and flooded several times.

Sea creatures seeking sanctuary found the caves an ideal habitat; some used them as temporary shelters, others took up permanent residence, evolving to suit this spelean — cave-dwelling — existence. The nature of life in blue holes depends on two principal factors; the amount of light available and whether the water inclines to saline or fresh. The most

Top: *Lucayan Indians once used the partially flooded caverns as burial sites.*

Above: *Marine life is most abundant at cave entrances.*

Below: *Shell Hole, in the Bahamas, shows its blue maw in the clear shallows.*

meet is quite distinct and it is at this point, called the halocline, where the chemical action caused by the mingling of the waters combines with the agitation of the tides to dissolve away the limestone. Tunnels and, eventually, caves are created by this process and the erosion may even continue through the bedrock of the islands to open inland blue holes as well as those below the seabed. In ages past, changes in sea level have also helped

dazzling array of life is found at the entrances of oceanic blue holes such as Conch Blue Hole, off the north-east coast of Andros, the biggest Bahamian island. Every element of a coral reef is crowded into the opening, from anemones and flexible sea fan corals feeding in the tidal flow which wells through the system, to crustaceans, octopuses and the many fish that shelter in calmer crevices. Rays and nurse sharks can sometimes be found resting on the sandy floor. Further inside the caves, life becomes scarcer; though sponges, sea cucumbers and hydroids — cousins of coral — are all well adapted to this dark existence and grand old lobsters may also lurk here, wedged into rocky lairs. But even deep inside the tunnels, cave divers have seen snappers swimming languidly along, completely upside-down, using the cavern roof for guidance.

None of these species is fully adapted to cave life, but hundreds of metres inside the caverns one true cave-dweller is found; *Lucifuga speleotes*, the blind, white cave-fish of the Bahamas. Another true spelean creature was discovered in 1980 by Jill Yager, a marine biologist working in the Lucayan Caverns on Grand Bahama. It was a tiny crustacean like a swimming centipede, blind and unpigmented. Realizing it was a new species, she named it *speleonectes*, meaning 'cave-swimmer'. In fact, it turned out to belong to an entirely new order of animals which is now called Remipedia.

Inland, there are blue holes whose character is significantly different from their ocean counterparts. They may have no direct opening to the sea yet salt water wells up through the rock to fill the deeper passages while freshwater tops up the system from above. Here, where salt and freshwater meet, divers can swim through the transitional waters of the halocline. The entrances to inland blue holes are often found in mosquito-infested creeks and lakes; Andros is peppered with them. During the 1980s, Rob Palmer, a British cave-diver and explorer, led a series of expeditions to Andros to continue George Benjamin's pioneering work. The expeditions explored many types of blue hole, both oceanic and inland, but found more specialized fauna established in inland systems, such as the Sagittarius Caverns, which are home to three different species

Below: *Inland cave galleries may emerge above the waterline into dry caverns, reflecting conditions that contributed to the caves' formation when sea levels dropped during the last ice age.*

of Remipedia and swarms with many other tiny specialized crustaceans. By the end of the 1987 expedition, however, several of the more regularly dived caverns were beginning to show how fragile these environments are. The tiny fauna were less in evidence than before, driven into hiding by the disturbance, and several of the most slender speleothems had been shattered — not through carelessness, but simply by the pressure waves caused by a passing diver.

The exquisite fragility of these blue holes is part of their beauty, but it also means they are easily damaged. One of the lakes on Andros, which contains an entrance to the Elvenhome Blue Hole, has been used as a village rubbish dump for years and is quite polluted. Rob Palmer and many others who have worked in blue holes want to see them properly protected and conservation strategies are now being formulated. In addition, several long-term experiments are now underway in some of the blue holes. In Elvenhome, tiny limestone pills have been set into the cavern wall at different depths to monitor the effects of any chemical changes in the water. Elsewhere, tests are going on to discover if the rock is still being dissolved and whether new caves are being created at any level. In the fields of biology, hydrology and geology, as well as raw exploration, the lairs of the Lusca still have much to reveal.

Sarah Foster

FOREVER GLADES

The Everglades of Florida are one of the natural wetland wonders of our planet and their global significance has long been recognized worldwide: the Everglades were listed by the United Nations Education, Scientific, and Cultural Organization as a Biosphere Reserve in 1976; in 1979 they were declared a World Heritage Site; and, in 1987, more than 5000 sq km were designated as a Wetland of International Importance. Yet despite international recognition of its special value, the Everglades' future is far from secure and this unique ecosystem continues to be threatened by two powerful forces of change — human activity and devastating hurricanes.

The Everglades cover 10,600 sq km of southern Florida and together with the adjoining Big Cypress Swamp form the largest freshwater marsh system in the USA. Historically, the area has relied on the overflow of waters from the 1800 sq km Lake Okeechobee, the state's largest lake, during the rainy summer months. The whole area south of the lake is really a vast plain, sloping very gently towards the coast. The fall of only 4.5 m across nearly 200 km, however, causes the overflow to run off so slowly towards the Gulf of Mexico that, in some places, the water doesn't appear to move at all. This 'river' is some 80 km across but a mere 15 cm deep. The native Indians called it *Pa-hay-okee* or 'River of Grass', and it is here that probably the best known of

Right: *Water is the unifying element across the Florida Everglades, linking the dense freshwater stands of temperate trees, like these rising from a cypress swamp, to the myriad islands of the saline coastal fringe.*

Below: *The aptly-named Ten Thousand Islands fray the north-west coastline of the National Park.*

Above: *The freshwater swamps of the Everglades are the stronghold of the American alligator. Specimens up to 5.8 m have been recorded but one of 3.5 m is now considered large. The rarer and endangered American crocodile also retains its last foothold in the national park – mainly in brackish or saline coastal waters.*

all the Everglades' wildlife — the American alligator — makes its home.

In these conditions, an altitude difference of just one metre can bring about a dramatic change in vegetation. Indeed, biologists have identified eight different ecosystems in the Everglades, from tropical mangroves to temperate pine forests, all providing a valuable refuge for a unique mix of wildlife. The seasons, though, can be extreme — the land becoming parched and dry during the winter before the onset of the rainy season in late May or June, when over 80 per

cent of the yearly precipitation falls. The wet season also coincides with the hurricane season and during the early morning hours of 24th August 1992, Hurricane 'Andrew', the strongest hurricane to strike the state in half a century, roared into southern Florida.

Hurricanes often begin when warm air rising up from the tropics meets cold air from the north. Andrew started as a group of thunderstorms in western Africa around 13th August and moved out into the Atlantic as a rainy low-pressure wave. The United States National Hurricane Center tracks dozens of these waves every year via satellite. By Monday 17th August, this particular wave had developed into a swirling tropical storm, but at that time lacked the central 'eye' characteristic of hurricanes. The 'eye', similar to a chimney, forms when warm, moist air rises from the ocean surface and spirals up to a height where it condenses and releases its heat energy. But high winds prevented the chimney from holding together and swept the storm north across the ocean.

Suddenly, on Friday 21st August, the wind dropped and a high-pressure zone began to push Andrew towards the coast of Florida. Andrew struck the Bahamas at 240 km/h on Sunday evening and claimed four lives. The storm continued to gain strength as it sped on relentlessly through the Gulf of Mexico towards the coast, striking the southern tip of Florida early on Monday morning. Although 43 lives were lost, the toll could have been much higher had residents not heeded the emergency warnings prompting them to evacuate. After only four violent hours, the storm had left tens of thousands homeless, including more than a hundred National Park employees and their families.

Immediately following the storm, 20 scientists from the National Parks Service were sent into the Everglades to begin assessing the initial damage. Biscayne National Park, north of the Everglades, caught the entire wrath of Andrew, losing part of its mainland headquarters and the majority of its cover of subtropical trees.

One of the most striking direct effects of hurricanes in the Everglades is the major damage caused to trees, mainly in the hardwood 'hammocks' — isolated areas of hardwood forest on higher ground — mangroves, and pine forests. Andrew flattened over 260 sq km of mangrove forest, though fortunately some of these trees might survive: following the passage of Hurricane Gilbert through South America in 1989, 90 per cent of downed trees survived. Virtually all of the large hammock trees were affected and almost a third were downed or snapped like matchsticks in the 263.93 km/h winds (the official anemometer at the National Hurricane Center in Coral Gables blew apart at that speed!). Scientists believe that in some places, the wind gusted up to 320 km/h.

On the whole, wildlife was not severely affected by Andrew, although 200 wading birds at the Biscayne Bay roost and one deer were found dead. Of the 32 radio-collared deer all survived, though about one third moved their home range. Adult

Above: *Mature slash pines left broken like so much flimsy match-wood in the aftermath of Hurricane Andrew's 300 km/h winds.*

Below: *Rare inland, the attractive tricolored heron is a common year round resident of Florida's coastal mangrove swamps.*

Above: *The Everglades' white-tailed deer survived Hurricane Andrew, though around 30 per cent moved their home range.*

Below: *Hurricanes help fast-growing non-native tree species, like paperbark, invade areas that once held native species.*

and some corals will continue to grow even after they have become detached from the rocks. But increased turbidity — caused by sediment stirred up by the strong wind-whipped currents — persisted for over a month after the departure of the storm, blocking out sunlight and preventing marine plants from making food.

Andrew may even have had benefits for some animals. Sea turtle nesting beaches may have been improved by the sand which was washed deep inland in some wilderness areas. The mangrove fish community also remained largely unaffected.

It is possible that the most damaging effect of the hurricane is yet to come in the form of the spread of invasive plant species not native to the Everglades. Already present in the region are two particularly aggressive colonizing trees: the paperbark and Brazilian pepper. These trees grow much more quickly than native species and can soon overtake vast areas. This can affect birds' nesting and breeding sites as well as their food supply as the ousted native plants become scarce, or worse still, disappear completely. Such change can have a severe impact across the entire food-chain, and scientists are now monitoring the situation closely. Studies to examine the long-term effects of Hurricane Andrew on the Everglades have only just begun. $1.4 million dollars has been appropriated to fund a complete impact

alligators were unhurt but as their young were hatching when Andrew struck, their fate is open to question. The previous summer had already been a poor season for breeding alligators as almost half of all the eggs laid had failed to hatch, compared to a quarter in average years. Other preliminary assessments have indicated that the populations of some endangered species, such as the Stock Island tree snail and Schaus' swallowtail butterfly may also have been severely damaged.

Marine environments fared a little better in comparison with terrestrial systems. The damage which did occur was mainly through lobster and crab trap debris smashing into coastal corals and sponges and damaging or destroying these fragile marine animals. Some 200-year-old corals that had survived Hurricane Donna in 1960 (a storm which devastated the Florida Keys), were broken at the base. However, this may not be as detrimental as it first appears — many reefs grow naturally by regenerating after storm damage, assessment. Only when this data becomes available in the next three to five years will the full effects be revealed.

Florida has long been subject to violent tropical storms and has suffered more hurricanes than any other part of the United States. Hurricane Andrew alone is thought to have caused damage to property estimated at $30 billion. But natural disasters like Andrew, although having a devastating effect on urban areas, pose much less of a long-term threat to the natural environment compared to the hand of man. The Everglades originally extended almost 100 km north of Lake Okeechobee to Lake Kissimee and remained largely untouched until the early part of this century. Now, even the original wetlands south of Lake Okeechobee have been drained for agriculture — mainly subsidized sugar cane plantations. The resultant run-off has become polluted by herbicides and pesticides, some of which have been able to enter areas of the northern Everglades, where they have already begun to affect the vegetation. High levels of mercury have also been identified across much of the food-chain, from fish to alligators. One of the most worrying recent finds has been a dead Florida panther whose body

Below: *After the passing of Hurricane Andrew, an aerial survey to check possible losses among the endangered population of manatees revealed 209 of these aquatic mammals — the largest number recorded since surveying began in the mid 1970s.*

Right: *The green turtle, which may reach a weight of over 200 kg, could gain from the effects of Hurricane Andrew, as huge amounts of sand were driven inland to enlarge and improve its nesting beaches.*

Below: *Less than 30 Florida panthers are thought to remain in the Everglades. Now, even these few are threatened by the highly toxic effects of mercury passing up the food-chain.*

contained levels of mercury which would be toxic to humans. The Florida panther, a subspecies of the puma, is so endangered that it may number less than 30 in the entire state. Now, the National Parks Service is working closely with the State of Florida to enforce water-quality laws to help address the problems of pollution.

As well as pollution, the area is also threatened by water diversion. Freshwater not only flows across the surface of the largely porous limestone bedrock, but also underground towards the Atlantic. It is the pressure caused by freshwater flowing through the Everglades which actually protects the water supplies of millions of people in southeastern Florida as it prevents seawater seeping up through the rock; if this hydrological system is ever seriously upset, the region's water would very rapidly become saline.

Ironically, it is the demand for fresh water in the cities which is starving the Everglades of that resource. Increasingly, the Everglades have to compete with the populations of West Palm Beach and Miami, in southeastern Florida, for a limited water supply; only California, New York and Texas have larger populations than Florida. Furthermore, over 900 people move to the 'Sunshine State' daily, and an extra 750,000 litres of water has to be found to meet their needs every day. More and more residents of Florida's west coast are now drinking desalinated water. Seasonal demands cause problems too — in some years, 39 million people have taken their vacations in Florida and 12 million of these visited during the winter season when water supplies were naturally low. A series of canals has been constructed to channel Okeechobee's freshwater to the cities, yet the increasing urban spread prevents rainwater from reaching the underground aquifers, or water-bearing rocks. Now, the marshlands have to rely entirely on sensitive management to maintain the fragile ecological balance. Apart from pollution and water diversion, unnatural flooding through extensive crop irrigation is also a serious problem. Alligators, for example, build their nests at the highest natural water level. But if too much floodwater from irrigation run-off enters the system at the wrong season the nests are often washed away. The wood stork, too, is threatened by artificial flooding. Only wetlands which dry out seasonally into isolated ponds concentrate enough food (around 200 kg of fish) to feed a pair of these magnificent birds during the breeding season. When natural wetland cycles are upset, the wood stork, which has been on the endangered list since 1984, fails to breed successfully.

Much of the wildlife has been able to adapt to great storms like Andrew. But the specialized habitat upon which the Everglades' animal communities depend must be allowed to recover from the frequent natural disasters such as storms, drought and fire without the extra burden imposed by people. Only a fifth of the remaining Everglades lies within the boundaries of a National Park and is therefore protected from direct damage by human activity. However, National Parks are not islands and indirect external activity can still have a detrimental effect on the ecosystems which are within the protected areas.

If the Everglades are destroyed, it is not only the wildlife which would be lost: the thriving tourist industry would be crippled, large natural resource industries, like fishing, could not exist, and the general public health of the area would suffer. In the words of the National Parks Service: 'Just as we share the enjoyment of this natural resource, so we must share the responsibility for finding solutions to these problems'.

Alison Byard

Below: *Roseate spoonbills are threatened almost everywhere across their range, even in the Everglades which offers the bird its main North American habitat.*

TOWARDS A WARMER WORLD

Right: *According to some predictions, the effects of global warming would be felt most at the poles, causing the ice caps to melt and shrink. Other experts claim, however, that in a warmer world precipitation, including snow, would be higher, and that as a result the ice caps would expand.*

Below: *Analysis of air bubbles trapped in ice during the past 160,000 years has revealed that the amount of carbon dioxide in the air correlates closely with global temperature.*

1994 should see world governments finally taking action to tackle the greenhouse effect. But since the agreements to limit emissions of the main greenhouse gas, carbon dioxide, were made at the Earth Summit's Climate Convention in 1992, scientific opinion has become more strongly divided on the subject. Just what, then, do scientists know about the likely effects of warming on the earth?

First, no one denies that the greenhouse effect actually exists. Various gases in our atmosphere act like a blanket around the planet, trapping some of the sun's heat. These greenhouse gases include carbon dioxide, water vapour and methane. Without them, the planet would freeze. Second, human activity, particularly over the last 200 years, has added considerable amounts of carbon dioxide to the atmosphere through the widespread burning of coal, oil, gas and wood. Consequently we are clearly in danger of tipping the natural balance, but the debate surrounds what might happen as a result.

Measurements of the amounts of atmospheric carbon dioxide taken over the last 35 years have shown a steady increase each year. There are now more than 350 parts of carbon dioxide per million of air, roughly 25 per cent more than the figure before the Industrial Revolution. If we go on burning more fossil fuels we could increase the ratio to

about 550 parts per million by the mid 21st century.

Not all the carbon dioxide we unleash stays in the atmosphere though. The earth has a certain capacity to absorb a proportion of it in a variety of ways. Some seems to be absorbed by the oceans, becoming incorporated in plankton, coral and other marine life, while on land plants also utilize carbon dioxide in photosynthesis.

What would happen, however, if carbon dioxide levels were allowed to increase unchecked? Clearly there would be a major change to the chemistry of our atmosphere. But does this matter? The answer from the scientists is an unfortunately vague 'probably'. Basic physics says that the extra carbon dioxide will trap more heat and this, other things

Below: *In a warmer world tropical storms could become more widespread, striking regions previously unaffected.*

Bottom: *Forest fires release vast quantities of carbon dioxide into the atmosphere.*

being equal (which is unlikely), would warm the planet on average by about one degree over the next 50 or so years. To some extent this prediction is supported by recent research.

The problem with making predictions, however, is that there is a lot of natural variability in year-to-year, and even decade-to-decade, global temperatures that has nothing to do with the greenhouse effect. Sunspots, volcanic eruptions and changes in ocean currents all play their part in this. And despite all the record breaking temperatures of recent years, we have not yet stepped outside that normal range of variability.

What makes matters even more complicated is that when something as fundamental to the planet as its blanket of gases is interfered with, a lot of other things are upset as well. And these things, 'feedbacks', could in turn influence global temperatures. Some of these factors could well cause 'feedback effects' — positive feedbacks which would raise the earth's temperature or negative ones which would lower it. Some feedback effects are understood and can be allowed for in calculations; others are speculative. If the planet warms up, for instance, ice caps will melt. Ice caps, being white, reflect a lot of the sun's heat straight back into space. But if they shrink, the bare rocks underneath will absorb the heat. This will further heat up the planet, causing more ice to melt, more rock to be exposed and more heat to be retained, in other words a positive feedback.

More difficult predictions arise from the effects of warming on the rain cycle as no one is sure how it might work. But a hotter atmosphere will evaporate more water from the oceans and because water vapour in the air is a greenhouse gas, it could also act as a positive feedback. On the other hand, if the water vapour forms

Left: *The vast forests of Canada and Siberia could shrivel and die if global temperatures rise, releasing more carbon dioxide into the atmosphere. Some experts argue, however, that higher levels of carbon dioxide would act as a natural fertilizer and boost the growth of trees and other plants.*

more clouds, these would reflect more heat back into space, so cooling the planet — a negative feedback.

There are other feedbacks that could work either way too. Some involve the planet's living things, especially forests. Higher temperatures are likely to kill forests, especially the great northern forests of Siberia and Canada. These cover almost as much land as the tropical rainforests but are located where climate researchers predict global warming will be greatest. As the trees die, they would release carbon dioxide — a positive feedback. Before this happened, however, the increasing carbon dioxide levels might even act as a 'fertiliser' so that trees and other plants grew more vigorously, thereby outpacing warming by increasing their capacity to absorb yet greater amounts of carbon dioxide — a negative feedback.

Trying to determine exactly how all these feedbacks might balance out makes any predictions difficult. Indeed, the Intergovernmental Panel on Climate Change (IPCC) — the chief scientific

Above: *If non-polluting methods of generating energy, such as wind turbines, were combined with widescale energy conservation measures, emissions of carbon dioxide could be reduced by more than 20 per cent.*

advisers to the world's governments on the greenhouse effect — itself reflects the difficulties. The Panel's own figures for the rate of increase in global warming before the end of the next century range from 1.5 to 4.5 degrees Celsius. This range embraces such enormous differences in the severity of the climatic conditions which could result, however, that it has attracted criticism. Few scientists, though, disagree that the greenhouse effect is real and that there will be some warming. The

arguments rest with feedback effects and how much the warming will be. Prominent amongst anti-greenhouse effect critics is Richard Lindzen, Professor of Meteorology at the Massachusetts Institute of Technology in the USA. He argues that the atmosphere is much better at dissipating extra heat than the IPCC assumes and that clouds will provide strong negative feedback. Such critics may not be wrong, but they remain a small minority voice among scientists studying the issues.

Even if global warming does happen much as the IPCC predicts, it is not easy to translate the changes in global average temperatures into firm predictions about real weather in particular places. But scientists running statistical 'models' of the world's climate on super-computers have given us some idea of the possible changes we might expect. These show that warming will be greatest nearer the North and South poles, and most noticeable at night. So polar ice caps and the animals that live on them will be most at risk. In a hotter world, most of the climate systems that dominate our day-to-day weather will become more intense:

A HOLE IN THE SKY

The greenhouse effect and the thinning of the ozone layer are quite different, but linked, phenomena. Ozone is a natural gas that inhabits the stratosphere and protects the earth by filtering out ultraviolet radiation. If it disappeared, we would suffer many more cases of skin cancer and cataracts and many crops would not grow.

Recently, the ozone layer has thinned globally and, since the mid 1980s, a 'hole' in which the majority of the ozone disappears has opened up over Antarctica each spring.

Similar thinning has also begun over the Arctic.

The cause is industrial chemicals — especially chlorofluorocarbons (CFCs). CFCs are to be phased out before the end of the 1990s, but there are a lot already in the air — so the worst effects are yet to be seen. Ozone thinning has little effect on global warming, though there are two links between these man-made changes to our atmosphere. First, CFCs are also greenhouse gases. As they are phased out, one cause of global

warming will fade. Second, if the world does become warmer the atmosphere's temperature balance may be upset, making ozone holes more likely to occur.

deserts will become bigger and, if anything, drier; away from the deserts, it may be wetter. One estimate is that, globally, there will be 10 per cent more rain. Extreme weather of all sorts is more likely to occur. Tropical storms, such as typhoons and hurricanes, occur only when the sea temperature rises above 27 degrees Celsius. So in a warmer world there could be fiercer storms and more of them striking in new places.

Some places might even become colder in the greenhouse world. The reason could be a sudden switch in the global system of ocean currents that sustains the Gulf Stream, the strong current of warm tropical water that washes up the coast of western Europe as the North Atlantic Drift. If the Gulf Stream failed to penetrate farther north than Spain, then western Europe's climate could become as cold as that of Hudson Bay or much of Siberia, which are both on similar latitudes.

In the light of such uncertainty about the impact of global warming, are we to stand back until we are compelled by certainty to act? For some people debate is action enough until they can be sure — but we may be losing valuable time and ultimately face the prospect of doing too little, too late. Others feel that our very uncertainty should at least prompt us to adopt some sort of contingency programme as a safeguard. The IPCC told the Earth Summit that a 60 per cent cut in carbon dioxide emissions is required to stabilize the concentration of the gas in the atmosphere at current levels. And that is an undisputed fact. As the Secretary General of that Summit put it in his closing speech: 'The message has got to get through. The evidence is very powerful. We are on a course for disaster'. 1994 may, therefore, turn out to be an extremely critical year for the earth.

Fred Pearce

Above: *If sea levels rise many low-lying islands would be inundated.*

Below & overleaf: *Statistical models of the world's climate suggest that deserts will become bigger, hotter and drier, and that marginal lands will become barren.*

WILDLIFE & CONSERVATION ORGANIZATIONS

Many organizations concerned with wildlife welfare are taking less of a back-seat view when it comes to action. Practical initiatives are now in order and in this respect the decade has already seen some great leaps forward. In the face of gathering crises, the forces for change are ranging themselves squarely against the pressing issues of the day.

Birds are valuable indicators of the vitality of ecosystems but more than one in ten species face extinction. In response, BirdLife International is showing the wider global gains that can be achieved via its bird-led programmes. Rhinos continue to be slaughtered and World Wide Fund for Nature is determined to intensify its 30-year struggle to tackle this and other worsening problems, as are the 'wildlife sleuths' who aim to expose the trade in wildlife for profit. Around the world, Earthwatch projects are encouraging a more personal contribution to conservation and at grass roots level more people are becoming active too — by setting up hospitals for wild creatures.

The future, though, lies with the young, and if the torch of environmental consciousness is passed on now by those who care, then maybe their dreams for today will not turn into children's nightmares tomorrow.

Left: *Polar bear tagging and tracking off Svalbard, in the Arctic Ocean, allows researchers to follow the wanderings of this great carnivore of the north.*

Above: *Beast with a burden. In overcrowded Asia few elephants roam free; the majority are working animals. With nowhere to go and a status that falls between wild and domesticated, the Asian elephant occupies a precarious position that demands the urgent attention of conservation groups.*

Right: *Studies of the bottle-nose dolphin are revealing more and more aspects of their behaviour — which gives a clearer picture of their needs in the wild.*

THE WILDLIFE SLEUTHS

Below: *The EIA's efforts to combat the wild bird trade have done much to reduce the trapping and sale of bird species worldwide.*

Bottom: *Photographer Clive Lonsdale's secret shots, taken from a cardboard box, exposed illegal ivory-carving factories in Dubai and dealers in Hong Kong.*

Formed exactly ten years ago, the Environmental Investigation Agency (EIA) has in less than a decade proved itself to be a potent force in the fight to protect wild animals. Set up by Allan Thornton, the founder and former director of Greenpeace UK, together with Dave Currey and Jenny Lonsdale, the EIA recognized the growing need for a new breed of conservationist — the wildlife sleuth — to combat the cruel and often illicit exploitation of wildlife for profit.

Every year countless animals are slaughtered or perish in cargo holds because somewhere a middleman is willing to pay poachers handsome sums — secure in the knowledge that he, too, will make a fat return from the ready market for dolphin meat, a pet parrot, an ivory bangle or rhino horn medication. Not only is the wild animal trade cruel, in an increasing number of cases it is also illegal — as legislated by the Convention on International Trade in Endangered Species (CITES). Both these moral and legal judgements are vital levers for the EIA, whose aim is to move in on a trade racket, to film it and to find out who is involved. A truly international organization, the EIA presents its evidence of illegal operations to CITES and the world's governments since it is they who decide the fate of the planet's threatened wildlife.

Although the EIA's campaigns are limited in number, they cover a broad scope of issues and include the ivory trade, the killing of the world's cetaceans (whales, dolphins and porpoises), and the wild bird trade. But the EIA is a tiny organization far out of proportion to its international role, and its investigators cannot be everywhere at once. Accordingly, staff at the London offices use every resource at their disposal, compiling information from whatever source they can. Farther afield, the EIA has established a branch in Washington DC. The major benefit of a connection with the USA lies in the fact that the ordinary US citizen has unparalleled political access; the EIA can, in effect, write its own legislation and propose its additions to the statute books. Indeed, it drafted the outline legislation for the Wild Bird Conservation Act and lobbied the Senate relentlessly until George Bush finally approved it in 1992, in one of his final acts as President.

The detective work of Thornton and Currey really came of age during the EIA ivory campaign of the late 1980s, when they enlisted Jenny Lonsdale's husband Clive, a photographer, to help spy on Dubai's ivory-carving factories and dealers in Hong Kong. Often risking their personal safety, they shot film and compiled reports that revealed the systematic slaughter of elephants to feed the ivory market and led to the 1989 ban on international trade in ivory. Indeed, it was the mine of information gathered during the campaign that led to the 1992–3 campaign on the rhino horn trade, for the two issues are closely linked, from the scene of poaching through to the dealer's showroom.

Of the world's five species of rhino — the white and black rhinos of Africa, the Indian, and the Javan and Sumatran rhinos

of Asia — the black rhino has been hardest hit: of some 65,000 in 1970, only 3500 survive today — a loss of more than 95 per cent in 20-odd years. Total rhino numbers now may be less than 10,500 individuals, and, although habitat loss has been one factor, the blame for their steep decline can be laid at the feet of poachers.

The Chinese have used powdered rhino horn for over 2000 years to remedy many ailments. Today it is valued chiefly as a treatment against fever and sold by thousands of traditional doctors — many of whom lack a practitioner's licence. China is not the only consumer, however; currently four other countries are known to have imported horn in large quantities:

Taiwan, South Korea, Yemen and Thailand. Yemeni men have for more than 1000 years carved rhino horn handles for their ceremonial daggers, or *jambia*. Prized both as medicine and ornament, horn commands a huge price on the black market — about half that of gold.

The rhino's desperate plight topped the agenda of the newly formed CITES in 1975, and all species were put on Appendix I in 1976, banning international trade in any rhino-derived product. A further resolution in 1987 persuaded Japan, Hong Kong and Macau to ban domestic sales of rhino products. But 15 years of worldwide trade bans have done little to help elsewhere, only pushing the illicit

Above: *Biggest of all rhinos at up to 2.3 tonnes, the white rhino is so-called not because of its colour, but because of its wide — weit, in Afrikaans — square-lipped muzzle. Two races of white rhino occur in Africa, the northern and southern whites. Of these, the northern race is most endangered: only 40 may be left in the wild.*

Above: *The plight of all rhinos stems mainly from Middle and Far Eastern demand for products made from their horns. African rhinos, like these blacks, have two horns whereas Asian rhinos sport only one.*

trade underground. Illegal markets as far-flung as the USA and Europe continue to consume horn, but one of the greatest culprits is Taiwan.

The complex political history of this island lies at the root of the problem; annexed in the 1970s by the People's Republic of China, Taiwan has no independent seat in the United Nations and is therefore excluded from all resolutions issuing from the UN-funded CITES. But Taiwan has a booming economy and now has the largest foreign reserves of any country. With immense spending power and driven by the full force of Chinese

medical tradition, yet with no commitment to environmental protection, Taiwan has exploited the wildlife trade to the limit.

Under international pressure, however, Taiwan started to address the issue in the late 1980s with trade regulations and stock registration schemes, but, mistrustful of these measures, few medical practitioners bothered to register their stocks of horn. Moreover, the government did not penalize those who evaded its regulations. It has even been testified that in 1988 a small cartel of Taiwanese businessmen bought up several tonnes of Taiwanese horn stocks and exported them to China. This forced up the value of horn by more than 400 per cent to US$6000 per kilo, brought money to the cartel and fuelled demand for more horn. In short, dealers were accumulating wealth by banking on the extinction of the rhino.

Despite the efforts of conservationists, however, the rhinos' future remains bleak. In 1992 the Zimbabwean Government decided to dehorn its remaining black rhinos to deter poachers, but in doing so found to its horror that its stock, estimated at 1400–2100 animals, actually stood at only 430. The international reaction was instant. The UN appointed Dr E B Martin, a renowned authority on rhinos, to the newly created post of Special Envoy for Rhinos, and directed him to research the current status of countries known to consume horn. The previous year TRAFFIC, the wildlife trade monitoring programme, instigated a WWF-funded study into the consumption of rhino horn in Taiwan.

Left: *The atrocious butchery of a white rhino solely for its horn. Rhino horn is, in fact, not true horn at all but a tightly matted and compressed structure of hollow hairs, fairly loosely attached to the front of the animal's skull.*

Their report showed that 70 per cent of pharmacies acknowledged possession and that 1991 Taiwanese stocks of horn stood at around 10 tonnes, worth US$60 million.

Steeped in tradition and propped up by ruthless dealers, the horn trade debate

Above & left: *Small whales, like these pilot whales killed in the annual traditional hunt in the Faeroe Islands, had been given little attention until the EIA successfully raised a case for their protection at the 1990 meeting of the International Whaling Commission.*

Below: *Northern white rhinos are so rare that some now have personal guards for their protection.*

looks set to last interminably. But two things are quite clear: time is running out for the rhinos, and the CITES trade ban has not worked. From its experience of the elephant ivory trade the EIA believes that controlled trading of horn, which is advocated by some conservation bodies, will not help the rhinos either. The theory behind this arose in the 1980s and is still current in some quarters. It suggested that regulated culling of elephants would show the commercial advantage to be had from protecting wildlife — the expense of protection being offset by the official sale of the ivory gained. Thus the authorities gain, the local economy gains and the elephants remain secure. This argument is now being applied to rhinos by, for example, using the high fees willingly paid by game hunters to help fund anti-poaching squads. But the EIA has proved that Africa has little to gain from controlled trade as the poachers are

HEADLINE HISTORY: THE EIA'S CAMPAIGN MILESTONES

1986 First investigation of wild-caught bird trade in Senegal reveals full extent of the trade to the world.

1989 CITES agrees an international ban on the elephant ivory trade.

1990 EIA reports to the European Parliament on the wild bird trade. Lufthansa airlines, the world's largest carrier of wild birds, suspends its operations.

1990 Slaughter of dolphins in Peru — film and information released via worldwide news. Peru subsequently rules against dolphin killing.

1990 EIA's report, *The Global War Against Small Cetaceans,* released at the IWC meeting in Iceland. Historic breakthrough follows as the IWC establishes a precedent for their protection.

1991 Investigation into driftnetters operating from Mauritius leads to a ban on driftnet vessels.

1991 Campaign with RSPCA and RSPB to ban the wild bird trade persuades EC Parliament to ban trade. Most major airline carriers of wild birds pull out of the trade.

1992 EIA campaigns for five resolutions on direct killing of cetaceans and another on environmental threats to them at the IWC. All are passed.

1992 Aeroflot, the last major international airline to transport wild birds, suspends its service. Over 100 airlines now refuse to carry wild-caught birds.

1992 After heavy campaigning by the EIA, the UN passes a global driftnet ban. Countless marine species are saved.

1992 EIA co-sponsors the African Wildlife Enforcement Conference, bringing together agencies from seven African nations: this first conference proves to be a great success.

often not local Africans but outsiders whose profit benefits only themselves and their loot passes into the purses of other countries. So it is highly unlikely that such poachers would be deterred by joining a local programme to protect the elephants. The EIA's message, therefore, is clear: kill the market in rhino horn, not the rhinos. But to tell Chinese consumers that rhino horn is worthless is a challenge which must be handled sensitively if education in the marketplace is not to be mistaken for an insulting disrespect for an old culture. No one, though, can ignore the fact that the horn supply may soon dry up forever.

The EIA entered the horn campaign in late 1992, armed with files on the smuggling network between Africa and the Far East, and singled out Taiwan as the main target.The EIA had a strong ally in David Shepherd, with his high public profile as a popular artist and television personality. Thornton's intention was to push for a British trade ban on Taiwanese goods by revealing that the Taiwanese were implicated in the crime of gaining at least some of their wealth directly from rhino-poaching. In November of 1992 the EIA released its campaign publication entitled *Taiwan Kills Rhinos — With Your Money*. Within three days the Taiwanese government imposed a ban on internal trade in rhino horn. But though the campaign brought the issue sharply into focus, it fell short on one vital ingredient: Taiwan established no method of enforcing the ban. The EIA has since launched a second thrust through its USA office, counting partly on a clause in American law which allows the

USA to impose a ban on imports from any country seen to be contravening an international resolution that protects threatened species: Taiwan would be sorely affected by a loss of trade with the USA. Should such a ban come to pass, time must surely run out for those countries that persist in ignoring international wildlife law.

Workers at the EIA are positive that the world can work for wildlife if it cares to try. If in 20 years time the African plains are once more stocked with rhinos, it will be because a concerned public was moved to pledge its support for the initiatives of a few angry sleuths.

Matthew Turner

Above & top: *A safeguard against poaching is to fit rhinos with radio transmitters so that their whereabouts in the wild are known at all times.*

SAVE THE BIRDS, SAVE THE PLANET

Opposite: *Relatively few restricted range bird species occur in temperate regions; most are found in the tropics. But the population changes in the skylark may indicate a widening problem as, over 20 years, it has declined across Europe by up to 50 per cent due to changes in farming practices.*

Below: *Ju-ju dancers in the Kilum Forest wearing traditional wooden masks.*

In a remote village in the Bamenda Highlands of northern Cameroon, the dust rises as a group of local people performs a dramatic traditional ju-ju dance. On their heads the dancers wear wooden masks representing brightly coloured birds. Meanwhile, in the forest that crowns the nearby mountain-top, a villager carefully tends a hive of honeybees, while, thousands of kilometres to the north, in an office in Cambridge, England, a scientist checks a database for details of the wide variety of birds found in the same forest.

Each of these is a vital element in a programme aimed at saving the area's rich forest habitat. The Kilum Mountain Forest Project is run by a number of international agencies and governments working in concert with the local people, who have the most to gain from its success. For over 100,000 people the forest is literally their life-support system, providing them with food, fuel, wood, medicines, shelter and a spiritual homeland. Once widespread in the Bamenda Highlands, forests such as Kilum have now been all but destroyed by the advance of farming and forestry.

The bird masks worn by the ju-ju dancers represent Bannerman's turaco, one of the world's most threatened bird species. This beautiful pigeon-sized distant relative of the cuckoos is shy and difficult to observe, its soft green plumage blending with the dappled light of the dense forest foliage, but, when seen, it reveals a stunning red crest, blue face, yellow bill and red wing patches. Along with another globally threatened bird, the banded wattle-eye, the turaco is found only in this small area of remaining forest, as are many other unique animals and plants. Kilum is a treasure house of biological diversity and the villagers' recognition of the birds' importance as symbols of that diversity is now playing a vital part in the region's conservation.

The Kilum Mountain Project has addressed major problems such as maintaining forest boundaries, reducing the threat of fire and limiting the damage done by the villagers' goats and sheep. Soil conservation and improved methods of farming have already minimized soil erosion and impoverishment, enhanced productivity and reduced the need for

Above: *The American harpy eagle flies within the lowland forests of Central and South America, where it is now localized, to seize prey such as monkeys.*

Below: *Capture for trade and habitat loss has forced the decline of the Australian Gouldian finch.*

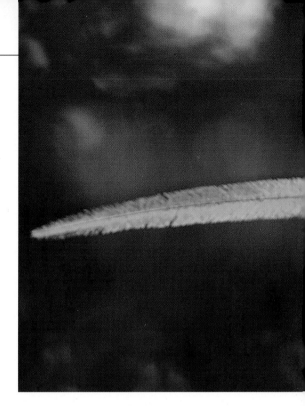

further encroachment on the forest. Several tree nurseries have also been established to restock the forest, and the ancient arts of gathering traditional medicines, producing hand-made paper and wood carving have been encouraged, bringing in much needed income while helping to preserve the rich and complex natural forest ecosystem. Bee-keeping has been particularly successful; to ensure a good crop of honey, the bees must have a wide range of tree and plant species that flower at different times of the year. All this should preserve the sustainability of the forest, thereby ensuring that the rich variety of birds and other wildlife of Kilum, along with the human population, survives.

All over the world, similar projects are underway, involving local people in saving their heritage of threatened birds, together with the whole range of other wildlife and the habitats that sustain the entire community. Many of these projects, including Kilum, are coordinated by BirdLife International, the first truly global bird conservation organization, which was launched around the world on 3 March 1993. This organization evolved from the International Council for Bird Preservation (ICBP), the world's first international conservation organization, founded in 1922. Over the years, ICBP grew into a federation of organizations dedicated to saving the world's birds and their habitats. Its base, in Cambridge, has now become the world headquarters of the new organization, while regional offices have been established in Washington DC (USA), Brussels (Belgium), Quito (Ecuador), and Bogor (Indonesia). Represented in 112 countries, BirdLife International is the leading authority on the status of the world's birds and their habitats and is tackling the huge problems facing birds everywhere — over 1000 out of the world total of 9700 species are threatened with imminent extinction.

A vital feature of this ambitious rescue mission is the national partnership scheme whereby existing national bird conservation organizations sign up to BirdLife International's policies. They share the

animals or plants. Indeed, many of the advances gained in the fields of ecology and behavioural biology have resulted from studying birds. Comparison of birds and other living things shows that, in many cases, the abundance and distribution patterns of birds reflect those of other less well known animals and plants.

The single most serious threat to birds and, therefore, to biodiversity is from accelerating habitat destruction. Tropical forests are most at risk and these are home to no less than one in four of all bird species. Another threat, particularly on islands, is from introduced animals that either eat the birds, their eggs and chicks or compete with them for food. Oceanic islands contain 38 per cent of the world's threatened birds and of these more than half are restricted to just 11 groups of islands. Added to the pressures of habitat

Left: *The resplendent quetzal is protected by law but this long streamer-tailed Central American bird remains vulnerable to illegal trading and destruction of its upland forest home.*

Below: *No bird that becomes properly airborne is heavier than the great bustard; large males may weigh up to 18 kg. In Europe it is increasingly rare — particularly on the Spanish steppes, one of its former strongholds.*

BirdLife mandate and the organization's identity, including the eye-catching flying tern logo, as well as supporting its research and conservation programmes. In the UK, BirdLife International's partner is the Royal Society for the Protection of Birds (RSPB), already firmly established as Europe's leading wildlife conservation organization. With a programme of international work spanning 14 years, the RSPB is currently involved in projects in more than 30 different countries. Yet despite its large size (870,000 members) and economic and publicity clout, the RSPB doesn't have a hope of saving the world's 1000 endangered bird species by itself. But by working with BirdLife it is contributing to a fighting chance of achieving this end.

Birds are the best indicators of biodiversity because, thanks to their power of flight, they are so widespread in all habitats, they are highly sensitive to any environmental change, and more is known about their classification and distribution than any other major group of

Top: *The Andean condor is the world's biggest bird of prey and flies on three metre wings. Though not endangered it is becoming scarcer in the high mountains of the Andes.*

Above: *Caribbean rainforest is disappearing fast and along with it will go the very restricted St Vincent parrot.*

destruction and the effects of introduced animals, other threats such as hunting and the effects of pesticides can tip the balance inexorably towards extinction.

For many years, a popular conservation strategy was to focus on single 'flagship' species, such as the African elephant, the tiger or the giant panda. Although this approach has been very important in raising public awareness and dealing with threats to specific areas, it is no substitute for saving whole ecosystems. Also, while the increasingly successful and sophisticated programmes of captive breeding and reintroduction have a vital part to play in saving wildlife, they can help only a tiny fraction of species currently in peril. Increasingly, there has been a realization that it is essential to save entire ecosystems if biodiversity is to be maintained. But given

finite resources and the seeming impossibility of halting or slowing down much human destruction of wildlife habitats, particularly since the richest areas for biodiversity are mostly situated in the tropics, in poor Third World countries where population growth is highest, two pressing questions arise: where are the most important ecosystems that should be saved and are some of these more important than others?

BirdLife International's pioneering research project uses birds as indicators of biodiversity to identify the areas and ecosystems with the greatest concentrations of unique species. There are 221 such areas that are 'hotspots' for bird diversity. They are known as Endemic Bird Areas, or EBAs. ('Endemic' means restricted to a particular region.) Each EBA has at least two restricted range birds and such species are defined as those with a breeding range of less than 50,000 sq km. It is a sobering thought that nearly one third of the world's birds are restricted range species. The 221 EBAs between them contain 95 per cent of all restricted range birds. About 20 per cent of all bird species are restricted to 2 per cent of the earth's land surface and the places that make up this incredibly rich fraction hold 70 per cent of the world's most threatened birds and a high percentage of threatened mammals, reptiles, invertebrates and plants. Consequently, effective conservation of the EBAs will yield a correspondingly high return, in terms of conserving biodiversity, for the money and effort invested in them. Some EBAs though, are more important than others in respect of the severity of threats that may be levelled against them relative to the endangerment of the species that they contain. Only one quarter of EBAs lie in northern temperate countries: the great majority are in the tropics, with the southern tropics alone holding 42 per cent of the total. Only a tiny proportion (8 per cent) of the total area occupied by all 221 EBAs is protected and even the level of protection within them varies markedly.

An important part of the BirdLife biodiversity project, therefore, is geared to identifying primary areas of concern, so a computerized database of the 2609 restricted range bird species has been created to help pinpoint these spots. Information stored in it includes English and scientific names, the numbers of related species in the same genus, and of genera in the same family, countries where each bird breeds, habitat type (coded into ten broad categories) and degree of threat. Detailed information on the distribution of restricted range birds has also been compiled over a three-year period. A database holds 50,914 records of every locality where each species has been seen, collected, trapped for ringing or tape recorded. Other information includes precise geographical coordinates of location, breeding status, notes on abundance and names of observers. Also, range maps have been plotted for all species covered in the project, by transferring records from the distributional database into a Geographical Information System computer mapping programme. Ninety-three of the world's 144 bird families contain restricted range species although some families contain proportionately far more than others.

BirdLife recognizes that there is little time to lose as conservationists have estimated that current rates of extinction for birds and mammals are 100 to 1000 times their level under natural conditions; that is, without the effects of humans. Even if an estimate of the world's total species list is taken as a very conservative ten million, extinctions based on the above rates would still run at hundreds of species per day! But a major problem is that the countries that contain the most biodiversity are also chiefly those with the least resources to devote to their protection. The real challenge facing conservationists, then, is to work together on an international basis to ensure the necessary expertise and resources reach the areas where the conservation need is most pressing. BirdLife's ambitious programme aims to meet this challenge worldwide, bringing together all who care for birds and their habitats in a common cause to conserve threatened birds and their habitats, together with the rest of the earth's priceless wildlife heritage, for the future.

Jonathan Elphick

Below: *The loud and melodious strains of the Seychelles magpie-robin's song may not be heard for much longer as it is seriously endangered.*

A FUND FOR THE FUTURE

Opposite & below: *Part of WWF's long-term Korup Forest Project, located in Cameroon, aims to secure a future for threatened species such as the leopard, the rainforest zebra wood, and the red colobus monkey.*

With several million members across the world, the aptly named World Wide Fund for Nature (WWF) is one of the biggest and best-known of all conservation organizations. Since its beginnings in 1961 it has become renowned for resolutely working for the welfare of wild animals. Some of its beneficiaries, such as tigers, rhinos, elephants, eagles and, of course, giant pandas, are well known; but many, many more have received equally important attention, including far less glamorous creatures such as snakes, sharks and insects.

Increasingly, though, WWF is becoming known as an organization that combines care for individual species with a broader approach. It has become increasingly clear that simply saving species isn't enough — it is critical to save habitats too, and yet at the same time work realistically within the political and economic constraints of the modern world. WWF has therefore gradually changed the emphasis of its work. 'We haven't forgotten species', says Janet Barber, WWF's Programme Director, 'we've just started using more imaginative ways to protect them. We are constantly refining our approaches to make sure that we are as effective as possible. It is not simply a matter of saving species and habitats by buying land and then keeping people out; perhaps in the past that was seen as the way to do things, but today we cannot work in a vacuum.'

Now, the way forward is perhaps best expressed by WWF's own plans for the future as embodied in 'The Mission for the 1990s'. 'The Mission has a goal', Janet Barber says, 'to stop, and eventually reverse, the accelerating degradation of our planet's environments, and to help build a future in which humans live in harmony with nature.'

The world's forests, oceans and freshwater habitats are high among WWF's priorities for action. And one of the most important and imaginative of WWF's current projects, the Korup Project, illustrates this broad-based approach in action.

Located in Cameroon, Korup is the richest remaining African rainforest and covers an area as big as metropolitan London. The forest is home to over 250 species of bird and among its many mammals are leopards, golden cats, sitatunga — a spiral-horned antelope — and colobus monkeys. The life of a forest is, however, based on its plants and Korup has more than 400 species of tree alone.

How did WWF become involved in Korup? 'A few years ago we heard that

Above & top: *Hauls of poached skins, and ivory from the African elephant, underline WWF's ongoing policy to support species preservation as well as habitat conservation.*

there were plans to build a road through the forest', says Barber. 'That drew us in, and then we started talks with the Cameroon Government. Our concern was to get across the idea that Korup has many potential benefits that could easily be lost if the place were to be opened up. The commitment of the Cameroon Government to the project — and their support for it — is critical. It really is a long-term project. We've been there less than ten years, but it's going to take at least twice that long before we can say

that it is fully and successfully established.'

Korup has considerable potential to exploit its resources sustainably and WWF is helping to find ways of doing it. Carefully managed tourism is one way. As more and more people in the West become aware of the importance of rainforests they tend to want to see them and their wildlife first-hand. Ecotourism could therefore contribute to the economy. Another source of income could be derived from the controlled exploitation of the forest's plant products. Already nearly 100 natural substances of potential value to industry or medicine have been found in Korup, and 38 of these are new to science. Who knows what else awaits discovery? Making the rainforest work for its living is becoming increasingly necessary in a world where there are so many demands on land that some people see 'idle' reserves as a waste of space.

Over recent years, conservation bodies have learned that the goodwill of local people is critical to the success of nature reserves, as Janet Barber points out: 'We talked to the people who live in and around the reserve. We wanted to know what they wanted from the place. Inevitably we've ended up with a large and complex project. Our jobs range from setting up nurseries to grow forest fruit to persuading governments, international bodies, businesses and our members to give money to make the project a success'.

WWF operate in another equally important, though far from threatened, environment: the media. 'WWF is a huge organization', says Diana Lowe of WWF's communications department; 'if we don't tell the public what we are doing we simply don't get any money'. WWF want to reach a wide audience. 'We want the general public who aren't already members to know what we're doing, and we want to reach politicians, because so many decisions that affect the environment are made by governments. We also want to reach people in industry, because businesses provide us with important funds, which we need, of course, to do our work.'

Many stories about the natural world are very visual, and WWF makes use of this. 'For the big stories, we produce our own WWF video press releases; this means that quality images are available for the TV people to use to illustrate a story.' The sort of story that justifies the production of a video news release might be, for example, a meeting of the International Whaling Commission, where nations that wish to protect whales often clash with those that wish to hunt them. The story can be given extra impact on TV with WWF-shot videotape of threatened whales.

Diana Lowe also points out that conservation messages are not always easy to get across. 'We have to remember that the issues are not as simple as they sometimes appear to those of us in the West. If you're an African farmer struggling to grow

Below: *A black look from a Korup drill — its glossy jet-black mask distinguishes the drill from the other stump-tailed baboon species: the mandrill.*

enough crops for you and your family to live, and you wake up one morning to find that an elephant has trampled through your plot, eaten what it fancies and crushed the rest into the ground, how are you going to be convinced that elephants are things that we should keep!'

WWF also has to maintain media interest in its work but it is notoriously difficult to keep any news item in the limelight for very long. Worse still, as Diana Lowe comments, is the fact that, 'Fewer and fewer newspapers have environment correspondents now. So we have to be imaginative about making our stories of interest to business, agriculture, science and political correspondents, too'.

WWF reaches its members not only through the local, national and international media, but through its own devices. *WWF News* goes out to members — and to a wide range of other individuals and companies — keeping them up to date on WWF's activities; in effect, telling them exactly where their money is going. 'Members as individuals can help WWF', says Janet Barber, 'by spreading the word about conservation and by being green, aware people themselves. Also, of course, their subscriptions and donations are crucial to WWF's work.' But, 'Getting new members during a recession is difficult', says David Taylor, WWF's Director of Finance and Services. 'People, naturally enough, are reluctant to part with money when times are hard. But once we get them, we are very successful in keeping members.' This reflects the fact that WWF

members are supportive of the organization's work, even when money is tight.

For any membership organization, retaining members once recruited depends on keeping them happy and well-informed. *WWF News* aims to do this. Recent issues have focused on such diverse creatures as sharks, whales and butterflies, and the work of TRAFFIC is often featured. 'TRAFFIC stands for Trade Records Analysis of Flora and Fauna in Commerce', says Melanie Newman, of WWF's press department; 'it is the world's largest wildlife monitoring project, and its job is to monitor the trade in endangered species of plants and animals. TRAFFIC has no powers itself, but its investigators alert the authorities to any breaches of the wildlife trade laws. The investigators often operate undercover; for example, they may pretend to want to buy wildlife-based goods. A tremendous number of animals are in danger from illegal trade, including elephants, rhinos, big and small cats, snakes and primates. Many plants, such as rare wild orchids, are also threatened by collectors. Some are traded when they are not supposed to be traded at all, while others are traded in amounts far above those considered to be sustainable. The reasons for the trade are as varied as the species which are traded, and range from the use of powdered rhino horn as a medicine to the use of cat and reptile skins for coats and accessories. And although animal skins are rarely seen in some countries today, as a result of powerful campaigns against their use, the same is not true everywhere. Even in countries such as Italy and Greece, such fashion articles are still considered tasteful, and

Below: *Polar bear research on the Norwegian islands of Svalbard, supported by WWF as early as the mid 1960s, has subsequently revealed a dramatic increase in the area's denning sites.*

the illegal trade can help to supply the market.' Like a good many of WWF's operations TRAFFIC is independent, but WWF funds it as it is often more efficient to let such groups do the specialized work while it takes an overview.

Despite having grown into a huge and complex organization, the mood within WWF is far from complacent. WWF staff are aware, however, that they are still working against the odds. The aims WWF sets itself present a huge challenge and one that is not getting any easier. 'When WWF started', says Diana Lowe, 'one of the main concerns was the rhino. Today, 30 years later, it still is. Now we are having to tell people that if we do not act effectively to stop the trade in rhino horn, rhinos are going to become extinct.' The problem may still be there, but at least the rhino is still there too; if WWF had not been around it might already be extinct.

WWF's work goes on, and will no doubt have to continue into the distant future. But as long as conservation organizations like WWF exist, there is a chance that the wonderful diversity of life on earth will be preserved long enough for us to discover a less damaging way of coexisting with it.

Dr Tony Hare

WILDLIFE WARDS

Opposite: *As one of the UK's ten most threatened species the otter needs all the aid it can get. Expert attention by wildlife rehabilitators helped this orphaned pup to return safely to the wild as a strong and healthy adult.*

Below: *Increasingly common victims of road accidents, foxes often sustain serious injuries but wildlife hospitals are adept at improvising medical techniques and equipment — like this wheelbarrow 'wheelchair'— to aid them.*

In January 1993, the sinking of the oil tanker *Braer* brought a new organization face-to-face with its first national emergency, as members of the European Wildlife Rehabilitators' Association (EWRA) raced to the Shetlands to rescue and treat casualties of the spillage.

The formation of the EWRA in October 1992 marked an important stage in the development of the care of wildlife because its members, from countries as far apart as Greece and the former Czechoslovakia, made the first agreement of its kind to operate under a code of practice. More than 200 rehabilitators joined the association in its first six months, ranging from enormous enterprises, such as the Wildlife Hospital Trust, which treats 10,000 animals a year, to individuals who take in a dozen or so.

Coordination between independent wildlife groups has been growing for some years: in 1987 the British Wildlife Rehabilitation Council (BWRC) was established by a group of people, including Les Stocker who left to found the EWRA. Both organizations function as forums for discussion, allowing their members the chance to exchange views and share discoveries. But even though the BWRC has no policy regarding the way its members run their centres, the increasing sense of professionalism among wildlife carers is remarkable, especially considering that most of them work from their own homes. Still more astonishing is how fast the field of wildlife rehabilitation is expanding, with enquiries to all the organizations pouring in from people wanting advice on how to set up their own hospitals.

Fifteen years ago, the very concept of wildlife rehabilitation was almost non-existent. Despite the vast number of wildlife casualties every year, an estimated five million in Britain alone, there seemed to be nowhere apart from veterinary centres to take them for treatment. But most vets had very little experience of dealing with wildlife and, as no owners were involved, too often the treatment was to 'put the animal out of its misery'. Now, many vets welcome the work of rehabilitators, as it helps relieve their already heavy burden of work dealing with domestic animals. The Royal Society for the Protection of Birds also refers enquiries about injured birds to local wildlife hospitals.

Public awareness of the rehabilitators' work has also grown at a remarkable rate, fuelled by the environmental movement of the late 1980s and by features in all sections of the media. Since wildlife centres rely exclusively on private funding, this

kind of exposure has proved highly beneficial. Awareness also means that people are much more likely to take a casualty to a centre. Indeed, the rising number of casualties admitted to wildlife hospitals may be due as much to new caring attitudes as to worsening accident figures.

Britain's 'first-generation' wildlife hospitals were mostly started in the 1970s; among them were the New Quay Bird and Wildlife Hospital in Wales, St Tiggywinkle's in Buckinghamshire — now the Wildlife Hospital Trust — and the Hydestile Wildlife Hospital in Surrey. All were begun by people who discovered animals suffering, refused to ignore them and, in the absence of any better option, decided

to offer help themselves. Commitment, years of practical experience and the support of interested vets has made them, and others like them, the front-line experts.

Alan and Jean Bryant began working with seabirds at New Quay after a workable method of cleaning oiled birds was developed at the University of Newcastle in the early 1970s. So many cases were brought to their home that, in 1973, they had to decide whether to give up altogether or to set up a purpose-built

Below: *The young of any species, such as this leveret, are high-risk casualties. Daily weight checks help in assessing improvements.*

Top & above: *Hedgehog experts at the Wildlife Hospital Trust administer anæsthetic before setting broken limbs. Hedgehogs are remarkably resilient animals which can survive terrible injuries.*

clinic. Fortunately for the birds, the Bryants had a disused outhouse which they decided to convert into a hospital. Some five years later, the *Christos Bitas* spill vindicated their decision to continue. Although they had intended to concentrate on seabirds, the Bryants ended up treating all kinds of birds — and even a seal pup, christened Moses, which arrived in a basket. After he was returned fit and healthy to the sea, the Bryants thought they had finished with seals but since then they have treated 300 or so, and now have a fully-equipped seal unit, complete with tanks and heated pens, attached to the hospital. Alan feels that no further buildings are necessary on their 2.5-hectare site but remains flexible: 'We try to keep adaptable — you never know what's coming through from year to year'.

Lyn and Graham Cornick of the Hydestile Wildlife Hospital are widely regarded as the UK's foremost authorities on fox rehabilitation. But, like so many people involved in this area, their route to this position was quite circuitous. In 1978, on their way home from a party, they found a deer that had been knocked down by a car. There was nowhere locally to care for the deer and some people even laughed at them for trying to save it. However, as Lyn was a veterinary nurse, the couple decided to treat the animal themselves. As always, word soon spread and as more casualties turned up on their doorstep their home eventually became a hospital. By 1986, the hospital had become a charitable trust with a proper fund-raising system. Things were looking good until, in October 1987, the hospital's ambulance was destroyed by the hurricane which blasted south-east England. Gallantly, the South East Co-op came to the rescue — providing a new ambulance, and another replacement a few years after. Perhaps more importantly, the Co-op also began long-term sponsorship and now meets all the administrative costs of the hospital's fund-raising section, the Friends of Hydestile.

Today Les and Sue Stocker are leading lights in wildlife rehabilitation, but they too started out 15 years ago with a single casualty: Purdie, a female kestrel. The birds and animals which followed her were originally treated in the kitchen and kept in cages around the house and in the back garden, then, later, in a series of pre-fabricated cabins, also in the garden. Les's fascination with hedgehogs led to him setting up an intensive care unit for them in 1984, when drought in the UK caused many to suffer. Named St Tiggywinkle's, it caught the public imagination and gained not only local but national fame. 'It's always worth treating a hedgehog; they're amazingly resilient little creatures and can recover from the most horrific injuries', says Les. The Stockers' long-held dream had been to build a wildlife hospital with teaching facilities for veterinary students and rehabilitators alike. At a proposed cost of £1 million, it seemed likely to remain a dream, but persistence and fund-raising finally paid off and the Wildlife Hospital Trust opened at the end of 1991, with facilities to treat 10,000 animals a year. Training courses are planned to start early this year.

During the 1980s, rehabilitation centres multiplied as general interest in wildlife grew. Caroline and Tim Gould, who now run Vale Wildlife Rescue, had studied falconry and kept birds of prey for some years, so when in 1984 someone brought them an injured tawny owl they were already well equipped to look after it.

Unfortunately, one of the bird's wings was so badly damaged that it had to be amputated: the owl could not be released and so became a permanent resident at the Goulds'. They named him E.D., short for 'Ever Decreasing', because all his attempts to fly ended in ever-decreasing circles. Shortly after E.D.'s arrival, a local vet began passing on all sorts of wildlife casualties to the Goulds. By 1989 the Vale Wildlife Rescue had been set up and was registered as a charity by the following year. The number of patients grew accordingly; 1443 casualties were treated in 1991 and 2401 in 1992. To meet the growing numbers a £20,000 appeal was launched and, after many difficulties, Vale Wildlife Rescue finally moved to a new home in Tewkesbury, Gloucestershire, in November 1992. The Goulds have exciting plans to create a nature reserve on the site with a lake and marshland and Shell Oil is sponsoring the construction of a bat roost. In the near future, observation hides will be erected around the area.

In 1988, a virus threatened to decimate the North Sea population of common seals and many affected animals were found languishing in coastal waters. Roy Gravener, a Corby-based scuba diver, organized a team of volunteer divers and vets skilled with marine mammals to help rescue the sick animals direct from the sea.

Top: *Swans often live in close contact with humans and many suffer as a consequence. Common injuries include those caused by swallowing fishing hooks, lead-shot poisoning or damage from flying into overhead power lines.*

Above: *De-oiling seabirds is intensive work and, sadly, an all too common job for wildlife hospitals.*

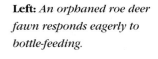

Left: *An orphaned roe deer fawn responds eagerly to bottle-feeding.*

Top & above: *An injured owl, like any bird of prey, demands very careful treatment and must be fully recovered before it can be released. If the injury involves the loss of a wing or talon, the bird can never be freed. Special licences are needed, though, to keep such species for more than a few days.*

Right: *No creature is too small or ugly to be denied the hand of friendship.*

This grew into British Divers Marine Life Rescue (BDMLR), a mobile rapid response unit. Although the virus crisis has now passed, BDMLR continues to rescue marine mammals and is planning improvements to its rescue centres.

Located off the Scottish coast, the Skye Environmental Centre, run by Grace and Paul Yoxon, is actually a field centre for study courses and wildlife holidays. They, too, became involved with casualties of the seal virus. Now the Scottish Society for the Prevention of Cruelty to Animals sends them injured animals of all kinds, including seals, birds, deer, foxes, hedgehogs and otters, many of which come from the mainland. The centre's future was threatened in March 1992, when the local planning authority ordered the removal of its Portakabin clinic by 1994. The proposed solution involves converting another building at the centre into a hospital; it would allow more space for casualties than before and thus be an improvement — but at a cost of £50,000. Fund-raising efforts were well underway in 1993 and the Yoxons hope to raise the full amount before time runs out.

The Royal Society for the Prevention of Cruelty to Animals has three hospitals of its own, in Norfolk, Somerset and Cheshire, the last of which opened in 1993. But the Society still makes use of independent rehabilitators, especially if an injured animal would otherwise have to travel a long distance to one of its own centres.

The transportation of injured animals is problematic. Opinions vary on how far an animal should have to travel for proper treatment, but the proliferation of hospitals can only help shorten such journeys and lead to faster, better care. Cooperation between centres is vital for this reason and some rehabilitators will offer advice on the phone to a colleague dealing with an unfamiliar problem, in preference to subjecting an injured animal to the stress of a long journey to the specialist centre. Before any journey is undertaken, though, casualties are given first-aid and treated for shock.

Large wildlife hospitals take in any casualty that comes along, but many smaller centres operate as specialists because they lack space or resources. Hospitals may specialize for many reasons; some because particular expertise is on hand, others because of location — being close to the sea, for example. Even legal issues can influence the species a hospital may take in. For example, birds such as hawks, falcons, kingfishers and corncrakes may only be kept by licensed Rehabilitation Keepers (LRKs), approved by the Department of the Environment. And by law all injured birds must be released as soon as they have recovered.

The range of treatments available today is as varied as the injuries and illnesses which rehabilitators see. Broken bones are extremely common and now even the tiniest limbs can be set — often with techniques invented for the occasion. New fields are also being explored all the time; Les Stocker is currently working on improving care for frogs and toads and various people are researching the best ways to treat and rehabilitate otters.

Many rehabilitators are involved with education, whether in schools, veterinary colleges, or through campaigns. This, in itself, can prevent injuries to wildlife caused by thoughtlessness or ignorance. One campaign, for example, sought to alert people to the dangers of feeding hedgehogs bread and milk — which gives them terrible indigestion — suggesting canned dog or cat food and water be given instead. Wildlife care is not included in veterinary courses, but students who want to learn more can now gain experience by working in wildlife hospitals.

As yet, there are very few careers in wildlife care, although as hospitals expand this is bound to change. Such a life, though, will not be for those seeking wealth and fame for the work is motivated by concern and round-the-clock devotion. But rewards come every time a badger recovers from a broken hip, a fox is healed of mange, or a kestrel flies free on a mended wing, and another life is saved.

Sarah Foster

Left: Acknowledged fox experts are to be found at the Hydestile Wildlife Hospital, Surrey.

CASUALTIES OF CONCERN

Every year, wildlife hospitals are brought young animals of every kind that are not injured but seem to have been abandoned: the truth is that most of them have been 'rescued' needlessly.

When an animal is born, a great deal of time is spent by one, or both, parents finding food to feed it. Babies may therefore be left alone for long periods: this is perfectly normal. So if you find a baby animal on its own, it will usually be for a good reason as the parents are naturally attentive. Resist the first temptation to approach or touch it for if the parent is watching it may be scared away and fail to return to its young. If you really have cause for concern, watch the animal carefully to see if it is injured; if all seems well, leave it alone for a time before taking further action — at least two hours for a small animal and up to 24 hours for a large one, such as a seal. If

it is in immediate danger and you must move it, handle it as little as possible and always with gloved hands, so that your scent is not transferred to its skin. Move it only as far as necessary; its mother will find it, if it is in calling distance from where she left it. If a baby bird (not a fledgling) has fallen out of its nest, try to find the nest and return the bird to it.

If the baby has been orphaned, or is visibly injured, then a call to your local wildlife hospital is the next step. Simply taking the creature home to tend it yourself may cause problems on release, even if it survives. This must be done by a trained rehabilitator.

In most cases the wildlife hospital would try to arrange any rescue measures itself, but if this is simply not possible, most will otherwise offer some good advice on how best you can deal with the situation yourself.

CHILDREN AND CONSERVATION

Opposite: *Nationwide pond-logging by young volunteers has revealed that 50 per cent of all the UK's ponds have disappeared over the past 100 years.*

Below: *The future welfare of wildlife and habitats lies with those young people, like these birdwatchers, who are prepared to take an active interest in their surroundings.*

Saving the planet from ecological disaster became the issue of the 1980s. The destruction of the rainforests, depletion of the ozone layer and global warming became familiar topics of conversation — going 'green' was suddenly fashionable. Political parties quickly laid claim to green credentials to gain votes, and the number of people applying to join environmental groups rose to an all-time high by the end of the decade. The enthusiasm and urgency with which these topics have been addressed has steadied in more recent years but, nonetheless, the past decade has left us with a vital legacy of a change in attitudes.

New attitudes to the environment were reflected in government policy — and for the first time environmental education became a subject for the classroom.

Although 'environmentalism' is not taught as a specific subject, the National Curriculum Council (NCC) identifies it as one of five 'cross-curricular themes' which can be incorporated into school projects. The NCC expresses the aims of environmental education with an almost religious zeal, referring to young people as the 'custodians of the environment'. Twenty years ago this sort of government lead would have been inconceivable; today it is a measure of the growing recognition that the sole hope of ending environmental destruction lies in the hands of children and young people.

Now, in schools all over the UK, children are actively participating in resolving real environmental problems as fieldwork provides them with the chance to develop an awareness and curiosity about some of today's issues. In over 60 secondary schools in Hertfordshire, an ambitious project to monitor the levels of acid rain involved establishing close links with schoolchildren in Norway. For a year children in both countries carefully analysed water pollutants, acidic precipitation and weather conditions. The results, which were displayed on graphs and videos, were shown to international scientists and representatives from the Norwegian Embassy. Although not every school can attempt so ambitious a project, even at a local level environmental education can ensure that young people develop the necessary skills which will enable them to protect and improve the environment in the future.

individuals and nations perhaps the terrifying statistics issued each year by the Worldwatch Institute (in *Vital Signs)* will be mitigated by active concern. The 1993 statistics make for depressing reading as they catalogue some of the disturbing trends that may shape our future. Now, time is running out so fast that today's young people are the last generation that can be invested with a chance of halting environmental destruction.

Fortunately, young people nationwide are joining conservation organizations with the aim of doing their part to turn the tide. The number of members in the Royal Society for the Protection of Birds' Young Ornithologists' Club, for example, swelled to 120,000 in 1993 — making it one of the country's largest conservation organizations. Under-16-year-olds with a passion for birds have participated in the YOC's annual bird survey since its introduction in 1979. Last year 11,000 young people throughout Britain spent an hour one weekend recording the number and species of each bird that visited their garden or local park to compile valuable statistics for conservationists. In September 1992 an hour spent by volunteers across the land logging ponds enabled the Wildfowl and Wetlands Trust to estimate that 50 per cent of our countryside ponds have disappeared within the last 100 years as a result of changes in farming practices and increased mechanization.

Members of the YOC often gain hands-on experience helping their local RSPB groups.

Above: *Species samples taken from local waters can reveal much about the well-being, or lack of it, of a much wider area.*

Right: *Less waste, less need. Green habits instilled in the young may curb the excesses of the current 'throwaway' generation.*

Environmental education has strong links with 'education for citizenship' — the NCC's term for introducing pupils to political processes and encouraging them to take on social responsibility. It is an impressive aim that is already being realized — the children who took part in the acid rain study soon gained an awareness of how emissions from power stations in the UK can cause acid rain in Scandinavia. If more young people become aware of the environmental interdependence of

Children from the Inverness YOC became part of an exciting project to save the black-throated diver. This rare and striking bird traditionally nests on islets or shores of Scottish lochs, but as it is highly adapted for swimming — with legs set well back on the body — it is a clumsy walker and therefore nests close to the water's edge. However, in seasons of high rainfall the divers' nests often get washed away. The Inverness group thought of an inspired solution to the divers' plight: they made floating platforms from wood and polystyrene for the divers to nest on. The birds took to the artificial rafts and in the first year of the scheme twice as many young were produced on the nesting platforms as on the natural sites. With only 150 pairs of divers left, continued successes like this could save the bird from disappearing in the UK.

Organizations such as the YOC also provide young people with plenty of lively educational material in the form of regular activity packs and fact sheets. A brief glance through *Bird Life*, the YOC

magazine, reveals plenty of hints on how to lead an eco-friendly lifestyle. This is one area where young people can make a real impact as they persuade their elders to become greener and also to join them on birdwatching expeditions. Parents of YOC members are also likely to find themselves checking that their roof insulation is adequate or saving water and energy by taking showers.

Some of the liveliest publications are those issued by WWF's Go Wild! club which describes itself as the wildest green club around. A branch of the largest conservation organization in the world, its 25,000 members range from 7-15 years of age. The club has recently updated its quarterly magazine, *Going Wild*, to include cut-out fact sheets, posters, environmental news and cartoons. Go Wild!

Top: *Sustainable growth. Children learn to use coppiced poles of timber to make strong fencing from natural materials.*

Above: *Reed cutting in winter. Young people help the National Trust carry out work that would otherwise be prohibitively expensive.*

Above: *Learning the old ways at the Ancient Technology Centre in rural Dorset.*

Below: *The Watch organization's education initiatives have been very successful in arousing children's concern for wildlife. Their Riverwatch scheme may one day help the hard-pressed otter.*

recognizes the importance of the voice of young people and encourages them to set up hearings where they can ask adults about the environmental issues that concern them. Like the YOC, Go Wild! encourages a range of activities that can be undertaken from home, such as planting a wildlife garden to attract butterflies.

Education is the key thrust in the work of Watch, the junior wing of the Royal Society for Nature Conservation, the UK's largest voluntary organization dealing with all aspects of wildlife conservation. Some 32,000 Watch members help to protect over 2000 key conservation sites throughout the land. The education team at Watch launch environmental initiatives specially designed to match the type of projects the NCC's cross-curricular themes require. The Watch organization has been so successful in rousing and sustaining children's concern for wildlife that a group of Russian environmentalists visited the Watch headquarters in Lincoln last February to learn how the group was tackling environmental issues. They were particularly impressed by Riverwatch, one of the most ambitious environmental education projects, which aims to monitor the state of the UK's rivers and then produce a national report.

Increasing numbers of young people are choosing to spend their holidays carrying out important conservation work for organizations such as the National Trust and Raleigh International. Each year the National Trust arranges more than 420 working holidays throughout the UK. Those designed specifically for young people are known as 'Young Acorn' holidays. Many of these involve outdoor conservation tasks such as dry-stone walling or managing a specific habitat. For those with more specialized areas of knowledge, there are holidays that involve botanical surveys, construction work and even archaeology. Young people from all over the country help the Trust to get work done which it could otherwise not afford. For those aged 17–25 who want to go even further afield, Raleigh International (formerly Operation

Raleigh) provides the opportunity for young volunteers, known as venturers, to take part in demanding environmental and community projects all over the world. On-going projects include research in the San Rafael National Park in Chile, where venturers are monitoring the San Rafael and San Quentin glaciers to obtain data on environmental and climatic change. In Zimbabwe, Namibia and many other countries Raleigh International carries out work in national parks and nature reserves, assisting with projects that help to protect and manage the areas for wildlife. In July 1993 Raleigh venturers joined the Mauritius Wildlife Appeal Fund and the Jersey Wildlife Preservation Trust on an expedition based in Mauritius. The projects included a survey of whale and dolphin populations in the waters surrounding Mauritius and a study of the rare Rodrigues Island fruit bat.

Mauritius and Rodrigues, island partners in the Indian Ocean, hold a diverse array of wildlife. Mauritius, particularly, is notable for three endangered species of bird: the Mauritius kestrel, the pink pigeon and the echo parakeet. In recent years these birds looked to be heading for the same fate as the island's most famous extinct species — the dodo — but a successful captive breeding and reintroduction programme has rescued the Mauritius kestrel and the pink pigeon from extinction.

Raleigh International sends about 900 young people on expeditions annually, but the number of places available is often hugely oversubscribed and up to 1000 hopefuls have to be turned away each year. The steady queue of young people hoping to become Raleigh venturers in Mauritius, though, is a pointer to a wider level of concern for the future and offers great hope that other creatures around the world may be saved from the same fate as the dodo.

Suzanne Jones

Above & left: *Young Acorn campers restoring dry-stone walling in Gloucestershire before earning time off to enjoy the delights of the countryside during their working holidays with the National Trust.*

MISSION TO EARTH

Opposite: *Earthwatch projects in Australia have helped show that kangaroos rarely compete with sheep for food. In turn, these findings may put an end to the killing of the one and a half million kangaroos that are unecessarily culled every year by ranchers.*

Below: *Research to discover whether dolphins' intelligence matches their brain capacity is a Honolulu-based project. Members assist in training dolphins, video-taping behaviour and caring for the animals.*

If someone suggested that for your holiday this year you spend two weeks in the rainforest of Borneo, trekking through swamps and undergrowth in 30 degree temperatures and 90 per cent humidity, watching out for lethal hazards such as snakes, toxic plants, fire ants, blood-sucking leeches and malarial mosquitoes, you would probably think they were joking.

But if you were told that this same trip offered you the chance to act as nanny to an orphan orang-utan, to collect vital data on the lifestyle of this rare species of ape, and to help in the struggle to save it from extinction, you might begin to think again and see the opportunity of a lifetime. And if you did you would not be alone. For over 20 years, an international charity called Earthwatch has given over 35,000 ordinary people the chance to use the time they would otherwise reserve for their holidays to take part in over one thousand conservation-based projects all over the world.

Earthwatch was set up in 1971 by Brian Rosborough, an American merchant banker. He felt that the only way to combat the lack of funding for environmental research was to establish a kind of 'merchant bank for the field sciences' — an organization that would bring scientific and environmental problems within reach of everyone who would be willing to invest not just money, but time and effort too, to help find solutions. This unique philosophy has enabled Earthwatch to expand from small beginnings in Boston, USA, into a worldwide organization that ranks with the National Geographic Society and World Wide Fund for Nature as one of the largest private funders of field research in the world.

There are now over 65,000 Earthwatch members worldwide. Over 50,000 of these are in the USA. In addition to its headquarters in Boston, Earthwatch has offices in Los Angeles, Melbourne, Tokyo and Moscow. In 1990 it opened its European office in Oxford, England, and now has over 7000 members in the UK. Membership is growing throughout Western Europe and volunteers are now being funded in Eastern Europe too.

Earthwatch calls its programme of scientific projects 'Mission to Earth'. The mission's goal is to improve our understanding of the planet and all the processes that affect life on earth. The projects Earthwatch funds are carefully chosen to fulfil this mission. Twice a year, its Centres for Field Research in Boston and Oxford invite proposals from scientists and those that are selected can be supported for many years by team after team of Earthwatch members — the

Above: *Members joining the Orang-utan Project, based in the Tanjung Puting National Park in Borneo, are involved in observing ex-captive orangs. They also follow and record the movements of wild orangs through the forests in order to help save these great apes and their habitat.*

EarthCorps — who pay to go and help.

Today, members can choose from over 150 scientific projects worldwide. To spend two weeks on a project, members contribute a proportion of the project costs — which can be as little as £300, though the average is about three times this sum. But joining an Earthwatch project offers much more than just the chance to visit another country — every member can enter the exciting world of environmental research which most of us normally glimpse only on television.

Projects include research on all sorts of wildlife and habitats from humpback whales off Western Australia, to elephants in Botswana, lemurs in Madagascar, lemon sharks in the Bahamas and birds in the Upper Amazon, to name but a few. Not all the projects are wildlife-based though; Earthwatch funds research in the fields of geology, archaeology and palaeontology too. While these projects are not as popular as working with wildlife, all have important research goals and need support. The 'Rise and Fall of the Himalayas' project hopes to discover facts about important global processes, such as glacial runoff and soil erosion. Not all the

projects are in remote locations either. Some are in, or very near to, large cities: In 1993 Earthwatch supported a new excavation of a medieval site right in the centre of Moscow's Red Square.

The projects vary widely when it comes to physical demands too. Some, such as the 'Sharks of Stone' project in Montana are very gruelling indeed. Volunteers spend most of their time breaking up rocks looking for fossils. On the 'Mountain Lion' project in Idaho, EarthCorps members spend six-hour shifts out in the snow radio-tracking collared animals. But Earthwatch stresses that you do not have

Left: *Polish hunters claim that wolves are killing the best red deer stags. Others say the wolves take the weakest animals. Earthwatch crews are taking a census of wolf and deer populations in the Bieszczady Mountains to find out the truth and so promote the welfare of both creatures.*

to be super-fit to join one of its projects. Some demand only gentle exertion and are suitable for people of all physical abilities, including the disabled. Volunteers on the 'Dolphin Intelligence' project in Hawaii help to train and care for a group of dolphins, while those on 'Saving the Leatherback Turtle' spend their time walking beaches at night on the Caribbean island of St Croix to monitor the turtles' nesting and hatching activities. The projects certainly attract all types of people, ranging from 17-year-old students to the elderly: one notable 82-year-old woman has been 24 times!

Left: *Just outside San Francisco, USA, Earthwatch teams are studying the Golden Gate National Recreation Area's two most abundant predators — the bobcat and grey fox — to find out how they interact. Volunteers help capture these creatures, fit radio collars and then track their movements.*

161

Top: *Observing sharks giving birth offers a valuable insight into their natural behaviour.*

Above: *Tagging and recording lemon sharks off the Bahamas helps conservationists monitor their numbers.*

All those who return from Earthwatch projects (and all have returned safely, despite the unforeseeable dangers that can crop up when working in the wild) talk not only of the enriching experience of encountering wildlife and nature close up, but also of the wonderful team spirit that characterizes all the projects. But Earthwatch is very much a two-way street. It is not just the volunteers who benefit from the experience. Most field scientists need to gather large volumes of data rapidly. Earthwatch volunteers can do time-consuming tasks which the scientists could never do themselves as quickly.

Despite being non-confrontational and non-campaigning, Earthwatch is becoming an increasingly influential global force for environmental change. The results produced by its scientists are contributing more and more to the pool of information that can be used by the various campaigning organizations. And it is not by accident that Earthwatch is contributing to this fight; some of Earthwatch's projects are directly targeted to effect change. The organization has an Advisory Group of scientists whose task it is to pinpoint crucial areas of environmental research that they feel will produce the solid information which the world's decision-makers need to help them plan the sustainable use of natural resources.

Adding to global knowledge on a governmental and scientific level is certainly a major achievement, though the spreading of environmental awareness can work in a very informal way — volunteers who gain hands-on experience in the field pass on their insights by word of mouth. Earthwatch is also working hard to make sure it reaches as many people as possible — not just those who can afford to go on one of its projects. Earthwatch Europe, for example, now runs 'Discovery Weekends' which feature talks and films together with various conservation activities, such as tree-planting.

But perhaps the most effective way of all to spread environmental consciousness is in the classroom. One of Earthwatch Europe's main activities is its Fellowship Programme. This new scheme channels money donated by businesses and trusts into sending students and teachers on projects. Educational bodies may also be given small 'starter grants', donated from the Fellowship Fund. Earthwatch is also increasing environmental awareness in the world of business. Many large multinational companies make donations and some send their own employees on projects, giving them an invaluable insight into the impact business and industry has on the environment.

In addition, Earthwatch is working to raise funds to provide scholarships and awards to enable less privileged people, both in developed and developing nations, to join projects. In Britain, it has teamed up with the Prince's Trust to send groups of disadvantaged young people on projects; and it is also seeking money from the European Community to help do the same for Third World citizens. To boost membership in Eastern Europe, Brian Walker, Director of Earthwatch Europe, has invited members to 'adopt' East European members by paying their membership fees.

Giving support to environmental scientists in poorer nations is now becoming a priority for Earthwatch. In Eastern Europe it has given support to projects in Bulgaria, the Czech Republics, Hungary, Poland and the former Soviet Union, while in China it is co-sponsoring a project with a local university. The organization also links up with other bodies in an advisory role. Its experience in sending members of the public all over the world ideally qualifies it to advise the growing number of eco-tour operators on how to ensure their holidays do not harm fragile environments.

Bringing the scientific information gathered from its projects to wherever it can best be used is Earthwatch's main aim over the next ten years. As a bridge between science and the public, it is still unique, and its philosophy of calling on ordinary people to share responsibility for the problems and challenges that face our planet provides an optimistic blueprint for conservation in the 21st century. If anything can save the planet, science can — helped, at least a little, by the dedication of Earthwatch and its members.

Hanna Bolus

Overleaf: *Studies of cetaceans, such as these spotted dolphins in the Bahamas, have revealed much about their current status, their social behaviour and the quality of their environment.*

Below & left: *Night teams monitor nesting leatherback turtles off Costa Rica while protecting nests from egg poachers and documenting details that will add to our knowledge of this endangered marine reptile.*

COMMUNICATORS & EDUCATORS

In an age of mass communication, the message of conservation comes in many different forms: from photographers and filmmakers; through people working actively in the field; via enthusiasts keen to share their passion; to the lost voices echoing down the years of those far-sighted prophets whose wise words have passed largely unheeded, but which ring ever true.

The work of wildlife photographers carries tremendous weight, as images have a daily impact on our lives. And, whether shot out in the field or within the studio, their material may inform, educate or shock us into a new way of seeing the world around us. National Park Rangers are charged with the duty of preserving some of the world's greatest natural wonders. Their expertise, born of day-to-day contact with nature, makes them guardians of a precious heritage. That such guardianship of our relationship with nature should be cherished was clearly seen by the pioneering environmentalist Aldo Leopold more than half a century ago. Even now, his thoughts provide a guiding framework which is perhaps more relevant today than ever before.

Expertise also comes in surprise packages, as celebrity Bill Oddie amply demonstrates in communicating his chief passion — birds and birdwatching.

Above: *Birdwatching days for school parties, such as those held at RSPB reserves, encourage young people to take an active interest in the natural world.*

Above right: *Aldo Leopold as Professor of Game Management at the University of Wisconsin, USA. Under his direction, the post was to become pivotal in turning the economically oriented conservation movement into one with an ecologically based approach.*

Right: *Field photographers in the Arizona desert, USA, filming elf-owls nesting in cactus cavities.*

LIFE OF A
PARK RANGER

Below: *Ranger Joe Craig holds a replica of one of the hundreds of thousands of Mexican free-tailed bats that roost in the Carlsbad Caverns.*

Bottom: *At dusk, spectators crowd at the cave mouth, in hushed anticipation, awaiting the bats' exodus.*

The National Park Service (NPS) now controls 368 areas in the USA, including all the national parks, preserves, monuments, seashores, lakeshores, rivers, battlefields, historical sites, and more. Over 3500 rangers work year-round in the parks and they are charged with the duty of preserving the national heritage of the USA and sharing it with all who visit.

A national park conjures visions of majestic snow-capped peaks and broad expanses of ancient forest but the reality is that every one is unique and no one can be chosen as typical; similarly, no park ranger is typical. But a look at the day-to-day life of one ranger in one park can give a rich taste of what the life may involve and illustrates the valuable role the NPS performs in the conservation of some of the world's most important natural sites.

A dashing figure, complete with broad-brimmed hat, cuts an impressive silhouette against the horizon as the sun sets. On stage, in front of 1500 people, ranger Joe Craig's voice carries a message of conservation, appreciation and understanding of a generally little cared for animal. As he speaks he knows that what everyone has been waiting for may occur at any moment. Then, like smoke billowing from a subterranean incinerator, thousands upon thousands of bats rise from the depths of the natural

entrance to the spectacular cave systems of the Carlsbad Caverns National Park. The bats steal the show and put an end to the programme that is staged each night during the summer as a preamble to the bats' appearance. Few such dramatic natural events are as predictable as the flying of the bats but, even so, Joe's talk must be flexible: he must talk until the bats decide

Left: *Part of the colony of around one million Mexican free-tailed bats inside the caves of the Carlsbad Caverns National Park in the south-eastern corner of New Mexico, USA.*

Below: *Outside the caverns themselves, park trails meander through the rugged ravines at the eastern edge of the Guadalupe mountain range which spans the borderlands of New Mexico and Texas.*

to fly, and this may be within 20 minutes or as long as two and a half hours.

As a boy of ten, Joe had visited The Great Smoky Mountains National Park with his father. It was there that his imagination had been captured by the charismatic ranger who guided their nature hike through the forest. From then on, Joe knew that he would someday wear the handsome green and grey uniform and the traditional 'Smokey the Bear' hat of the Park Ranger Service. He had no idea, however, how difficult it was going to be to realize his dream. He found out that applicants must be at least 18 years old and have a college degree or comparable work experience, specialist knowledge or both. What he didn't know was that every

Above: *Collared lizards are robust little reptiles, about 30 cm long, that are well adapted to the searing heat of the rocky desert terrain found within Carlsbad Caverns National Park. Males and females are different colours but both exhibit two black collar bands behind the head.*

Opposite: *A large desert cactus provides a safe armoured home for the cactus wren's nest.*

Right: *Carlsbad Caverns' boundaries take in part of the Chihuahuan desert — here flushed briefly green after refreshing, but rare, summer rain showers.*

get the job. For the next ten years Joe applied to a variety of different parks until finally, armed with a college degree in geology and three years' experience as a guide for a major camping tour operator, he was hired as an interpretive ranger at the Carlsbad Caverns National Park. Only then did he begin to discover the true scope of a ranger's duties.

Rangers are selected to specialize in one of three areas: interpretation — explaining to visitors exactly what they are seeing — resource management and law enforcement. There is a great deal of overlap but primarily a ranger deals with his or her speciality. At Carlsbad Caverns rangers are expected to run the visitors' centre, present evening bat-flight programmes, conduct nature walks, provide roving interpretation, perform law enforcement duties, conduct search and rescue operations, offer first response medical assistance, battle fires, and, between other tasks, complete a deal of paperwork.

position available was chased by least 300 applicants. On his 18th birthday he sent in two applications — for only two per year are allowed. He was sure that he had an advantage because of his intimate familiarity with the parks concerned. He did not

Once he was hired Joe began intensive training and was then assigned to a senior ranger on the 'buddy' system. It was the job of Joe's 'buddy' to teach him the ropes; it was Joe's job to tag along, to observe, listen and learn. Finally, Joe was ready to operate on his own, though he was soon to learn that much of his training would be on the job — as he discovered on the evening he was assigned to deliver his first bat-flight programme.

As he waited for the bats to wake, Joe explained to the audience that of the many bat species that have been known to roost in Carlsbad, seven are fairly common and the Mexican free-tailed comprises the vast majority. They migrate from Mexico in the spring and give birth in the caverns. Daily, at dusk, they exit *en masse*, leaving their young hanging from the ceiling, and head south-east to feed on insects before returning next morning. Towards the end of the season the young bats make their first flights and join the adults on their twilight sortie. Then, one evening, the bats make their exit from the cave and head back to Mexico and are not seen at the caverns again until the next spring.

Joe also spoke of the bats' history. When the caves were discovered there were an estimated five million bats roosting there, but after ingesting DDT and other pesticides via their insect prey, along with indiscriminate killing and man-made changes to their roosting environment, the population dropped to an estimated one hundred thousand. Later, after a ban on DDT, the colony grew to around one million.

171

Above: *Fire-fighting is all part of the job for a Park Ranger, not just within the park itself but wherever supplementary help is needed.*

to share his specialist knowledge with the visitors. Ongoing work on the restoration of the cave was another task that Joe performed. Over the years a great deal of debris had been left in the cave from the building of trails and bat guano mining, and its removal demanded hard work, while rebuilding some of the damaged rock formations required practical skills.

Nature hikes, similar to those Joe took as boy, are regularly scheduled at Carlsbad. Joe enjoyed the opportunity these gave him to explain the special adaptations of the plants and animals in the desert surrounding the caverns. Many visitors began the hike believing that all deserts were empty, but by the time they reached the end they had a different view. With his growing skill as a communicator, Joe could turn most people's vision of a barren wilderness into a picture of a richly stocked garden complete with beautifully

For nearly 90 minutes Joe enthusiastically churned out fascinating titbits of biology, history and geology before the bats finally awoke from their slumber deep within the earth and began their exodus at a rate of about 10,000 bats per minute. The stream of furry flying creatures ran unbroken for as long as Joe's talk. When the spectacle was over, his duties kept him at the site until the last visitor was gone — deep into the night.

On days when he was not assigned to the bat-flight programme, Joe began at 6.45 am by opening the visitor centre. Home to exhibits, auditoria, a gift shop, a restaurant and a book store, the visitor centre is an important link between the rangers and the public. The ranger staff of around 20 then move into the cave to take up positions for roving interpretation. Free to choose their own topics, each ranger tends to have favourite subjects, but most can talk endlessly about many. Joe's routine usually took him into the main 'room', a giant chamber, to talk about the formation and development of the cavern. As a trained geologist, this gave him the chance

adapted animals — all in a single afternoon.

Joe was also a member of the park's firefighting crew — which fought fires not just in the park but throughout the whole region. One especially dry summer sparked a spate of forest fires throughout the western states and one day Joe's crew was deployed to the Wenatchee National Forest, Washington. Upon their arrival, the rangers found themselves facing an inferno; a dense forest in rugged terrain was ablaze. For the first time, Joe realized his job demanded that he risk his life, but there was no question of setting to work immediately, digging and building firebreaks in an attempt to contain a fire that raged over an area bigger than a thousand football fields. The 12 to 14-hour days were back-breakingly hard, especially under the hot and dangerous conditions, and the battle with the fire lasted five days before it was brought under control. Then it was time for the dirty work of mopping-up; every square metre of the burned area had to be checked. Underground root systems can smoulder for days before suddenly flaring up to start a new fire. Slow, tedious and seemingly never-ending, the work went on and on and even then all danger was not past; widow-makers, trees that have burned on the inside but are still standing, posed a constant threat. Showing little or no external damage, such trees have no strength and the slightest breeze can bring them crashing down, crushing anything or anyone below. At this fire a widow-maker lived up to its name, killing one of the firefighters. Joe walked away with his life, and a new appreciation of his duties.

Rangers are famous for taking their pay in sunsets, for the salary is meagre. But the opportunity to live and work in one of the USA's parks is reward enough for many. For those who want to buy a home and raise a family, however, the base level pay

CARLSBAD CAVERNS

Unlike most national parks, Carlsbad's real splendour is hidden beneath the surface, for here lies the largest cave in the USA and the third largest in the world. The cavern is big enough to hold 14 football fields and was 250 million years in the making. Much more than a big hole in the ground, the huge mineral-deposit formations create a colourful, unworldly landscape — like a vast subterranean cathedral — that both moves and amazes its visitors. The caverns are home to few creatures but, above ground, mountain lions roam and more than 300 species of bird have been seen locally.

Deadly western diamondback rattlesnakes and the rare rock rattlesnake hide in the shade waiting for a meal of great plain skink, collared lizard or kangaroo rat. Tarantulas and scorpions crawl among the rocks and out in the surrounding desert the persistent call of the cactus wren pierces the dry, dusty air.

is prohibitive at $18,000 a year and many rangers have to leave the service early in their careers in order to make enough money to live a semi-normal life. Such was the case with Joe. After three years as a ranger he left to take a job making maps. Now as a manager of an Army corp's lakes and river projects he lives with his wife in their home in Little Rock, Arkansas. If he has any regrets they must include losing everyday contact with the wild and the wide-eyed wonder of adults and children alike on coming face-to-face with nature's grandeur.

Jeff Hall

Opposite: *In the shade of a flowering cactus a western diamondback rattlesnake coils itself in readiness to strike. This snake is responsible for more human fatalities than any other North American snake.*

NATURE IN FOCUS

Images of nature surround us. They appear on our television screens, in books and magazines, and confront us on posters. As the image has succeeded the written word as the currency of mass communication so those people who use images to please, persuade or shock us know just how effective portraits of the natural world can be.

Despite the fact that we live in a world dominated by video, the still picture has retained its potency. For while video gives a generalized description of an event, a still picture summarizes it. An excellent example of a still photo's ability to influence was provided several years ago by the International Fund for Animal Welfare, whose shocking photo of a baby fur seal about to be clubbed to death by a sealer provoked such a public outcry that the Canadian government was forced to review its policy.

Aside from such directly confrontational images, wildlife photography has much to offer on a more general level. Initially, there is the immediate attraction for the photographer of visiting wild places to create pictures of the animals or plants; subsequently there is the pleasure or knowledge to be gained from the information content in the pictures — a valuable exercise in itself. As nature photographers document the natural

Right: *André Bärtschi, Wildlife Photographer of the Year 1992, won the competition with this remarkable picture of red-and-green macaws in the Peruvian rainforest.*

Below: *Britain's biggest grouse, the capercaille, caught in shafts of sunlight in a Scottish wood, helped Neil MacIntyre take the 1992 Eric Hosking Award.*

Above: *A long day spent trailing this bachelor herd of wild asses in an Indian saline desert won first prize in the 'Endangered Wildlife' category for Joanna Van Gruisen — despite the searing heat which caused problems for both film and photographer.*

world they amass a record of what we have — and what we stand to lose. The pictures are reference points against which future change can be gauged. They are evidence of the world's beauty and the great diversity which it still possesses.

Technological developments have opened new fields of opportunity for the wildlife photographer to portray subjects under a whole range of weather and lighting conditions which were previously thought too difficult to tackle by all but the most seasoned professionals. In parallel with these developments, the number

of people engaged in wildlife and landscape photography has rocketed in the past ten years. Improvements in equipment have helped to level the playing field, in technical terms at least, between the amateur and the professional photographer, along with better and wider access to remote, foreign locations.

The current level of interest at once sustains and is fuelled by a proliferation of wildlife programmes, special interest magazines and books aimed at the general reader, naturalist and photographer. Many of these have appeared in recent years, while many other long-established titles are enjoying record circulations. It is not surprising then, that the standard of photographic illustration has risen with the number of photographers and nowhere has this been more clearly demonstrated than in the Wildlife Photographer of the Year Competition. Organized annually by *BBC Wildlife* magazine and the Natural History Museum, London, and sponsored by British Gas, the competition attracts more than 10,000 entries from full- and part-time photographers worldwide. It is truly a mirror of the state of the art. Unlike many photographic competitions, the panel of judges not only have a keen eye for aesthetic quality but also an extensive knowledge of the subject area, and so bring to bear an uncommon appreciation of the material as expressed in their selection of the winning entries.

Special sections offer encouragement to young photographers: for those of 17 years or under there is a chance to win the title of Young Wildlife Photographer of the Year; and for those aged 26 or under, a special Eric Hosking Award, in memory of Britain's best known bird photographer, recognizes excellence. Prizewinners and those with highly commended entries in any of the 17 sections of the competition are invited to a celebrity prize-giving ceremony at the Natural History Museum, where the photographs are exhibited. It is an unparalleled opportunity for nature photographers from all over the world to meet, exchange ideas and anecdotes, information and experiences; a rare chance indeed in what is otherwise a somewhat solitary pursuit. Importantly, too, success in the competition gives exposure to the work of young and part-time photographers, and provides a real impetus to the improvement of standards among all who enter it. The Wildlife Photographer of the Year Competition, therefore, has an important role to play in ensuring that ever-higher standards are promoted and that wildlife photography enjoys the wider stage which it most surely deserves.

So, what are the qualities of a winning photographer? André Bärtschi, Wildlife Photographer of the Year in

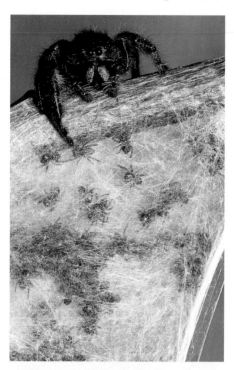

Below: *David Toney's jumping spider and her brood – taken in his own back yard. Home ground also gave Laurie Campbell this red deer stag (**bottom**).*

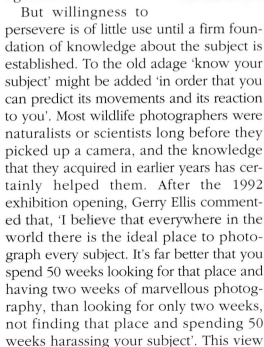

1992, whose images of macaws at a clay lick in the Peruvian rainforest captivated the judges, gives us a clue. He describes how, having located a site where these rare and magnificent birds descend from the canopy to take minerals from the clay, he built a hide nearby and visited it over a period of several days. On the morning on which he took his picture, temperature and humidity were, as always, very high. His sweat attracted dozens of bees and wasps eager to feed in it and which rewarded him only with stings, '...but after all, I got the photograph'. Successful photographers are not heroic; they are simply determined to take as good a picture as possible, secure in the knowledge that the pain of acquiring it will be long outlived by the pleasure of having obtained it. Perseverance, then, even more than patience, is a key quality.

Joanna Van Gruisen is another photographer who is undaunted by difficult working conditions. From early morning she trailed a bachelor herd of wild asses across the parched saline desert of the Little Rann of Kutch, India, gradually edging closer to the wary animals. By early afternoon, when she took her photo, the temperature had risen to 38°C and, in the absence of shade, caused problems for the film — let alone for the poor photographer.

A quite different set of extremes provided Finnish photographer Keijo Pentinnen with the awesome winter scene which earned him first prize in the 'Wild Places' category. In the cold Finnish landscape, condensed, humid air and snow combine to coat the spruce trees, here growing north of the Arctic Circle, transforming them into strange and magnificent pinnacles. The half-light at the time of year lends an ethereal quality to a picture which was taken in a way far removed from film box instructions to stand with the sun over your right shoulder!

But willingness to persevere is of little use until a firm foundation of knowledge about the subject is established. To the old adage 'know your subject' might be added 'in order that you can predict its movements and its reaction to you'. Most wildlife photographers were naturalists or scientists long before they picked up a camera, and the knowledge that they acquired in earlier years has certainly helped them. After the 1992 exhibition opening, Gerry Ellis commented that, 'I believe that everywhere in the world there is the ideal place to photograph every subject. It's far better that you spend 50 weeks looking for that place and having two weeks of marvellous photography, than looking for only two weeks, not finding that place and spending 50 weeks harassing your subject'. This view

Below: The bloody rivalry of male elephant seals, as witnessed from a Californian beach, won Kennan Ward the 1992 'Animal Behaviour: Mammals' category.

is endorsed by Neil MacIntyre, winner for the second year of the Eric Hosking Award. Although aware of a number of suitable locations where Britain's biggest grouse, the capercaillie, could be seen displaying, he sought out one where the birds would be least disturbed and where his hide would not attract the attention of passers-by. The capercaillie is a rare bird and one that is sadly in decline in Scotland; this sort of approach means that additional pressures are not placed on it by photographers.

The task of learning about one's subjects is made easier if they are close to home. David Toney of Colorado, USA, took his photograph of a female jumping spider and spiderlings literally in his own back yard, where he was able to monitor

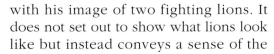

their development closely. The three Scottish prize-winners, Laurie Campbell, Neil MacIntyre and the author, also take most of their photographs locally. They appreciate the benefits of being able to return on a regular basis to a particular location — which is difficult and expensive if it is abroad. Visiting a particular site repeatedly also enables the photographer to view the landscape and its wildlife under all sorts of lighting conditions and at different times of the year.

But there is still more to wildlife photography than simple determination and good science. Who could doubt, on seeing Jan Töve Johansson's picture of yellow water lilies that an artist is at work? Such pictures challenge us to re-examine the way in which we view the natural world; leaves are not always green nor rocks grey. While it is relatively easy to move beyond a literal representation when photographing plants, it is altogether more challenging to do this with animals or birds. Gerald Hinde has met this challenge with his image of two fighting lions. It does not set out to show what lions look like but instead conveys a sense of the moment of confrontation — communicating a received feeling as well as relating a dramatic visual experience.

In a competition with over 10,000 entries, it is this ability to think beyond preconceived ideas about how things usually are, or should be, photographed which marks out the prize-winners. It is all too easy to miss the wood for the trees. Those who are able to shrug off limiting notions stand the best chance of producing the most original and stimulating work.

Below: *Bold tiger-stripe banding of light and shade forces the viewer's reappraisal of a sunset over sandbanks scene, here taken on the South Saskatchewan River by John Eastcott and Yva Momantiuk to earn runner-up in the category entitled 'From Dawn to Dusk'.*

To the qualities of perseverance, subject knowledge and an artistic eye, competence behind the camera must, of course, be added. While modern cameras are often easier to use in comparison with their forerunners, the fact that they allow photographers to push the borders of possibility ever further creates its own challenges. This is particularly the case with cameras and lenses which focus automatically. Capturing a picture of two sea eagles disputing ownership of a fish, as Konrad Wothe has successfully done, is daunting enough with an auto-focus telephoto lens, but next to impossible with a manually focused one for anyone who does not use a camera on a daily basis. The photographer, unable to approach the eagles closely, was obliged to use a big auto-focus telephoto lens with a magnifying power of x17 — presenting himself with the major challenge of following the birds in action while trying to prevent camera shake at the same time.

Although it is true that expensive cameras (and more particularly lenses) extend the possibilities open to their users, it is equally true that few people realize the potential of the equipment that they already own. That outstanding wildlife pictures can be taken with relatively simple tools is demonstrated in Kennan Ward's dramatic image of the clash of two northern elephant seals. Although he used a professional-grade camera and lens, the same results could have been obtained with more modestly priced equipment.

It is one thing to describe the characteristics of a good nature photographer, but quite another to pinpoint the qualities of an outstanding photograph. Some have been touched upon already. One which has been a consistent feature in successful entries over the years is eye-contact between the subject and the photographer. These pictures, such as Laurie Campbell's red deer stag, seem to have an ability to engage the viewer's attention in a way which other photographs do not. Luis

Left: *The eerie half-light of the northern Scandinavian winter transforms these hardy trees into semi-abstract frozen statuary and gained first place in the 'Wild Places' category for Finnish photographer Keijo Pentinnen.*

Below: *This limpid, painterly image of water lilies by Jan Töve Johansson won him a runner-up award in the category 'In Praise of Plants'.*

Miguel Ruiz Gordon chose to concentrate on the face of a caged chimpanzee to produce a picture which not only impresses in it own right but also has a powerful emotional content. In other cases the content of the image is so bleak — as in Richard Packwood's corsac fox in solitary confinement — that, eye contact or not, the effect is as powerful as it is depressing.

There is the constant appeal too of pictures in which we imagine we can see something of ourselves. Perhaps in Gerry Ellis' unobtrusive portrait of a young chimpanzee we can recognize feelings of our own. Other photographs owe their success to simple drama: it may be the result of lighting — John Eastcott and Yva Momantiuk's picture of the sandbanks on the South Saskatchewan River at sunset illustrates this — or a particularly poignant or heart-stopping close-up.

The lion must be one of the most photographed species of mammal in Africa, yet Samantha Purdy has provided us with a fresh insight, one which comes from spending long periods of time with the animals and earning their trust. Indeed, many nature photographers find being close to, and accepted by, wild animals is ample reward for the frequent disappointment and frustration that much of their work also brings.

Today, as more and more people take part in nature photography, the question might be asked, do photographers pose a threat to the subjects they photograph? Sadly, this does happen, particularly in the case of nesting birds, many of which are intolerant of disturbance. In some areas of the national parks of East Africa, for example, ground nesting birds have all but disappeared, such is the volume of traffic leaving the tracks to give wildlife tourists better views of the big game which they have come to see. Many of these people are photographers.

On balance, though, the sensitivity which the majority of nature photographers develop to the natural world greatly outweighs the carelessness of the few irresponsible ones in terms of the contribution they make to conservation.

Niall Benvie

Above: *The tragedy of the conditions endured by a corsac fox in Bratislava Zoo moved the judges to award Richard Packwood with the runner up prize in the category: 'World in Our Hands'.*

Right: *A powerful statement of a chimp's caged misery challenges our level of compassion for the animals we keep in captivity. Accordingly, Luis Miguel Ruiz Gordon won the 'Primates in Peril' category with this emotionally loaded attack.*

Left: *An unusually fresh look at a relatively common subject. Samantha Purdy's winning shot in the 'Animal Portraits' category reveals much in the face of a hungry lioness, exhausted after an unsuccessful chase.*

ONE MAN'S VISION

Deep in the Apache National Forest of Arizona, on a high ridge, a pair of forest rangers were eating lunch. As one of them gazed lazily down on the river below he noticed what he first thought was a young doe fording the torrent. But when the animal reached the bank and shook out a shock of grizzled fur, he realized his error: it was a wolf. In an instant she was joined by six full-grown cubs, and as the pack rough and tumbled in playful greeting, the young rangers reached for their rifles.

'In those days we had never heard of passing up a chance to kill a wolf. In a second we were pumping lead into the pack, but with more excitement than accuracy: how to aim a steep downhill shot is always confusing. When our rifles were empty, the old wolf was down, and a pup was dragging a leg into impassable slide-rocks. We reached the old wolf in time to watch a fierce green fire dying in her eyes. I realized then, and have known ever since, that there was something new to me in those eyes — something known only to her and to the mountain. I was young then, and full of trigger itch; I thought that because fewer wolves meant more deer, that no wolves would mean hunters' paradise. But after seeing the green fire die, I sensed that neither wolf nor mountain agreed with such a view.'

Seldom has the case for preserving the natural balance between predator and prey been so movingly put. Yet these words were not written this year, nor last, but nearly 50 years ago by a man described as one of the foremost conservationists of this century: Aldo Leopold. Sadly, however, we live in a world where there are still young men full of trigger itch who are keen to see the green fire die, but amongst environmentalists, at least, there are signs that this lesson has finally been learnt.

Although Leopold recounts his experience of watching the she-wolf die as an instantaneous rite of passage, it was actually many years, and many an anti-wolf campaign, later before he could finally put this encounter into context. Conservationists have taken even longer, but in 1994 plans are in hand to release ten pairs of grey wolves to roam free in the Yellowstone National Park, Wyoming. If the reintroduction proves successful, Yellowstone will be the only area in the lower 48 states which has a full complement of the fauna originally present when Christopher Columbus first stepped on to American soil.

Leopold's legacy to the modern environmental movement, however, extends far beyond a simple plea for wolf conservation. For within the pages of his seminal work, *A Sand County Almanac* (published by Oxford University Press), Leopold not only inspires in his readers a deep and passionate affection for wildlife and

Below: *Aldo Leopold hunting along the Rio Gavilan, Mexico, in 1938. It was on his earlier visits to this 'unspoiled wilderness' that Leopold first began to perceive the land as a living organism.*

wilderness, but he also provides an ethical platform on which we can build a new relationship with the natural world.

As the twentieth century draws to its close, there can be little doubt that the battle to preserve biodiversity and protect the planet from over-exploitation and pollution has reached a critical phase. But vital though practical conservation measures are, be they captive breeding projects or the protection of habitats, arguably the greatest challenge facing us

Above: *With a quotation borrowed from Thoreau, Leopold suggests that, 'In wildness is the salvation of the world. Perhaps this is the hidden meaning in the howl of the wolf...'*

Left: *Acquired as a hunting camp 'the shack' became a weekend refuge from 'too much modernity'.*

Above: *It was while he held the post of Professor of Game Management at the University of Wisconsin that Leopold developed his ecologically based views on conservation.*

Right: *Tree damage caused by deer to the Chequamegon National Forest, northern Wisconsin, in 1935, supported Leopold's view that in the absence of predators browse-eating game can and will ruin its own range.*

essay to *A Sand County Almanac*, 'One basic weakness in a conservation system based wholly on economic motives is that most members of the land community have no economic value.' It was a theme he expounded further in the book's foreword, 'Conservation is getting nowhere because it is incompatible with our Abrahamic concept of land. We abuse land because we regard it as a commodity belonging to us.'

Leopold's response to this ideological poverty was to suggest that we revitalize our relationship with the land, 'When we see land as a community to which we belong, we may begin to use it with love and respect. There is no other way for land to survive the impact of mechanized man, nor for us to reap from it the aesthetic harvest it is capable, under science, of contributing to culture.' It is a philosophy that has its roots in Thoreau, and the pioneer ecologists, and which today flowers in the writings of Arne Naess, and the Deep Ecologists. And although some of its

today is to redefine our attitudes to an increasingly beleaguered world.

This need is most apparent in the obvious bankruptcy of much current conservation thinking, as demonstrated by the way in which conservationists frequently resort to emotional or economic arguments to support the case for conserving a threatened species or an area of wilderness. The weakness in both these arguments is easy to see, for when an animal or piece of land has neither economic worth, nor emotional appeal, then the conservationist's case is lost before it is begun. But by clinging to such a limited, resource-based view of the natural world we have already condemned thousands of species and vast areas of wilderness to oblivion. Even 50 years ago this terrible tragedy was patently obvious to Leopold. As he wrote in 'The Land Ethic', the concluding

critics argue that it is far too idealistic in a world where wilderness is a scarce resource and poverty is rife, there can be little doubt that if we continue to treat the planet like a global supermarket, where everything has a price and may be bought by those with sufficient funds, then it will not only be individuals who are impoverished but the very quality of life on earth.

Leopold lived at a time when the western world was being transformed at a rate faster than ever before or since. Witness to these changes, he was able to comment both objectively and emotionally on the price being paid for so much progress. And it was from his observations that he developed his 'land ethic' underpinned by an almost spiritual reverence for nature. At that time, however, there still existed a 'wild frontier' and vast areas of true wilderness for Leopold to lose himself in. But with the advent of the railroads he saw the land and its wild inhabitants placed under a new pressure: the demands of the recreationalist. Leopold summed it

up thus: 'Recreation became a problem with a name in the days of the elder Roosevelt, when the railroads which had banished the countryside from the city began to carry city-dwellers, *en masse*, to the countryside. It began to be noticed that the greater the exodus, the smaller the per-capita ration of peace, solitude, wildlife, and scenery, and the longer the migration to reach them'.

As the increasingly ubiquitous motor car further laid waste to the wilderness, Leopold was prompted to muse that: 'Recreational development is a job not of building roads into lovely country, but of building receptivity into the still unlovely human mind'. Such succinct comments as these are the hallmarks of Leopold's style and help explain why, over 40 years since it was published, *A Sand County Almanac* remains as fresh as it is forceful. The collection of anecdotal essays which comprise the first part of the book relate to Leopold's experiences on the 120-acre Sand County farm which he bought in 1935. The farmhouse itself had burned to the ground some years earlier and the only building left standing was an

Above: *A founding member of the Wilderness Society, Leopold saw true wilderness — such as that which remained in Alaska — as the control against which humanity's experiment in civilization could be measured.*

Right: *Although Leopold believed that knowledge could transform our perception of the world, he was also capable of pure wordless wonderment, 'Our ability to perceive quality in nature begins, as in art, with the pretty. It expands through successive stages of the beautiful to values as yet uncaptured by language.'*

Below: *During the 13 years Leopold owned his Sand County farm he kept a detailed record of its wildlife, especially its birds.*

old cowshed which Leopold affectionately referred to as 'the shack'. Leopold bought the farm with the express intention of establishing a personal relationship with the land. For although he equated education and culture with increasing landlessness, he felt the need to experience the conservation ethic personally. For, as he put it, the definition of a conservationist is not best written with a pen but with an axe. And so it was that with axe — and shovel — Leopold put his theoretical principles into practice.

An incurable insomniac, when staying at the farm he would rise before the sun and, sitting at the table outside the shack, await the waking of the world. Many of his encounters with wildlife recounted in *A Sand County Almanac* come from such early morning vigils. Dusk was also a special time for Leopold and one of his most poignant tales relates to his evening observations of woodcock. As a boy Leopold's fascination with wildlife was matched only by his passion for hunting it. But while he hunted throughout his life his attitude to his quarry which, thanks to the wise counsel of his father was always sensitive, became almost reverential. After marvelling at the woodcock's spring mating flights, Leopold was moved to write: 'The woodcock is a living refutation of the theory that the utility of a game bird is to serve as a target, or to pose gracefully on a slice of toast. No one would rather hunt woodcock in October than I, but since learning of the sky dance I find myself calling one or two birds enough. I must be sure that, come April, there be no dearth of dancers in the sunset sky.'

From the intensely personal sketches which comprise the first section of the book, Leopold proceeds in the second part to paint with a broader brush, incorporating experiences drawn from his wider travels. Here Leopold is more

detached and didactic as he begins to build his ideas about the land and its inhabitants into a more cohesive philosophy. But even here evidence of his love of wild creatures and wilderness is never far from the surface. Leopold developed a particular affection for marshland, and cranes in particular, and mourned their loss at the hands of the drainage engineers who ravaged Wisconsin in the 1910s and 1920s. As he put it, 'Amid the endless mediocrity of the commonplace, a crane

marsh holds a paleontological patent of nobility, won in the march of aeons, and revocable only by shotgun. The sadness discernible in some marshes arises, perhaps, from their once having harboured cranes. Now they stand humbled, adrift in history.' Even in such poetic and personal moments, however, Leopold is always pointing the reader towards a deeper understanding of the world. It is clear that he was informed by a broad understanding of evolutionary theory and, what was at the time, the new science of ecology, and it was this perspective that framed Leopold's land aesthetic as well as his land ethic. 'It is a century now since Darwin gave us the first glimpse of the origin of species. We know now what was unknown to all the preceding caravan of generations: that men are only fellow-voyagers with other creatures in the odyssey of evolution. This new knowledge should have given us, by this time, a sense of kinship with other fellow-creatures; a wish to live and let live; a sense of wonder over the magnitude and duration of the biotic enterprise.' Sadly, even half a century later this sense of kinship has still failed to materialize.

If the first two sections of Leopold's book glimmer with insights into the wonders of nature, it is only in the concluding essays that his ideas finally catch fire, illuminating the reader with an ethical perspective of the natural world and how we might better behave towards it. In many ways *A Sand County Almanac*

mirrors the organization of nature. Just as ecosystems build from the simplest life-forms up to the most complex, so Leopold's book builds from the homespun tales of life on the farm up to his monumentally didactic concluding essay, 'The Land Ethic'. Here he finally draws all the threads of his argument together and weaves them into a complex whole. Recognizing that, 'There is as yet no ethic dealing with man's relation to land and the animals and plants which grow upon it.', Leopold offers to forge one. As he points out, ethics have evolved on the premise that the individual is a member of a community. A land ethic, therefore, simply extends this concept of community 'to include soils, waters, plants, and animals, or collectively: the land.'

As we approach the dawn of a new century it is vital that conservationists embrace this ethic. For unless we give up our role as conquerors, and learn to see ourselves as part of the natural world, all we will conserve will be a synthetic, ersatz version of nature, and the human spirit will be devalued as a consequence.

John Birdsall

Below: *Leopold asserted that it is undeniably 'a good thing for people to get back to nature', but he had severe misgivings about the 'retreat of wilderness under the barrage of motorized tourists'.*

AN INSIDE VIEW

Opposite: *The harvest mouse's minuscule size — around 57 mm body length without tail — and its insect-like movements, makes filming it in the wild extremely difficult.*

Below right: *Studio work enables the camera to look inside the harvest mouse's intricately woven nest.*

Below: *Inside the earth; a fox cub caught leaving its den by a camera hidden underground.*

We have become used to startling pictures of animals going about even their most intimate business, like termites or ants at work deep inside their subterranean tunnels, or close-ups of fish spawning in the gravel of a shallow stream. These images have taught us much about the way many creatures behave and what they may need to survive in increasingly difficult circumstances by revealing aspects of their lifestyles that are normally hidden from the human eye. Yet all this is due not to uncommon good luck, nor to mystifyingly complex camera work in the field. It is through the dedication and care, coupled to the use of the most up-to-date technology, of photographers who recreate nature in the studio. And who, in so doing, push us forward to a better understanding of the natural world and reward us with some remarkable photographs in their own right along the way.

Almost all the animals depicted on these pages were photographed in conditions that, despite appearances, were far from natural: the pictures were obtained by wildlife photographers working indoors rather than in the wild. Why, though, when the real-life stage is already set and populated with its cast of animal actors, should photographers put themselves to so much trouble?

Wildlife photography is concerned with recording the natural world, yet the very act of photographing or filming animals in the wild is likely to make them behave unnaturally. The sudden intrusion of a camera into an animal's world is disruptive, while the presence of the photographer can be quite terrifying.

The difficulties of photographing in the wild are compounded by the tendency of many animals to indulge their most fascinating habits in the least accessible places — underwater, up trees, or in dark burrows. Getting the camera into position to take a worthwhile shot is hard enough, but getting enough light on a dark, secret scene is even harder. Filming, in particular, often requires several kilowatts of lighting. Simply introducing the necessary gear can be immensely disruptive, and switching it on may even risk frying the subject! Even if all this can be achieved without scaring off the performers, the photographer remains at the mercy of their whims and fancies. All the equipment may have been set up at a prime site, but if the animals suddenly decide to move on, then there is little that can be done about it and a valuable chance may be lost for ever.

Top & above: *A female brown trout lies over the nest of eggs while a male waits in attendance behind. This very natural-looking shot was the result of careful preparation of a tank set up in the studio.*

In the past, wildlife photographers and film-makers could not be expected to get shots of rabbits giving birth inside their burrows, bats catching moths in pitch darkness or insect flight depicted in slow-motion, so there was little need for an 'invasive' approach or the development of special techniques. Pioneers, like stills photographer Eric Hosking, or film-maker Eric Ashby, could capture our attention with images obtained by working at distance, using telephoto lenses and natural light. The animals hardly knew they were there. Sometimes this is still necessary and even desirable: big, fierce animals, such as tigers or bears, can rarely be approached, and rare, vulnerable animals should be disturbed as little as possible. But if we are to learn more about the behaviour of the earth's creatures then new images — revealing what we normally cannot see — are needed, and often the only way to find these is to go in close, very close.

One way of doing this is to approach the animals in their natural habitat very gradually, to acclimatize them to the equipment and photographer. With some creatures this may not be too difficult, but most birds or mammals are extremely wary and for smaller animals particularly, this is simply not possible and another way has to be found. So instead of slowly introducing the camera into the animals' habitat the animals are gently introduced into the camera's habitat — the studio.

The main advantage of working in the studio — apart from comfort — is that the filming area can be arranged to suit the camera. This is particularly important when close-up shots are needed, or some specialized technique such as slow-motion or time-lapse photography is to be employed. For example, filming the breeding behaviour of freshwater fish in the wild can be almost impossible, even with a purpose-built periscopic camera. The water is often murky, there is rarely enough light, the electrical equipment gets wet and fails at the critical moment and, most important, the fish are likely to swim out of shot. By contrast, a studio tank set-up allows control over the water clarity, the arrangement of adequate lighting without risking lethal electric shock and the use of a reliable, straightforward camera set-up in the knowledge that the fish will remain in front of its lens.

Such an arrangement sounds artificial, but the ultimate judges of this are the fish themselves. If, say, the purpose of the shots is to capture breeding behaviour and the fish actually start to breed, then obviously all is well. In such instances the film-maker or photographer needs to be an experienced naturalist who knows how the subjects behave in the wild and just what their requirements may be. Indeed, this is probably the most important element of the whole process, because zoological knowledge is essential for recreating the animals' habitat convincingly in the studio.

Filming the breeding behaviour of trout in the studios of Oxford Scientific Films, England, depended on such detailed knowledge. The basis of the set was a tank 3 m long and the water within had to be filtered, oxygenated and cooled to exactly the right degree if the fish were to spawn. Furthermore, the water had to flow as if in a stream, and at the right depth over natural stream-bed material. The tank was therefore linked to a 4500 litre reservoir by a circuit of piping and all the accompanying vegetation and related fauna from the wild was added. Ultra-violet lights were positioned above the tank to ensure the health of the aquatic plants, and cooling fans and heat-absorbing glass screens were installed between the tank and the 10,000 watts of photographic lighting needed. Within the tank the natural habitat of the trout was recreated as faithfully as possible, partly to convince the viewer that the sequence was shot in the wild, but mainly to convince the fish themselves that they were in a 'natural' situation. The fish took some time to settle down, but eventually they acclimatized to the tank, the filming lights and even the mechanical whirr of the camera (fish are very sensitive to vibration). Ultimately the set convinced not only the trout, which spawned, but also a dipper, a small bird that feeds on aquatic animals and fish eggs; when introduced to the tank the dipper began hunting for food almost immediately, 'flying' underwater in a way that had often been seen happening in rivers in the wild, but never filmed quite so effectively in close-up before.

The final film was completed by material shot on location above the water, skilfully intercut with the studio shots to reinforce the illusion that the fish were spawning in the wild. Some might complain that using such techniques is somehow 'cheating', but the fact

Left: *A sequence of multiflash exposures at 1/60,000 second records the mighty leap of a flea.*

Below & bottom: *A living branch of oak placed right in front of the studio camera enables extreme close-ups of the tree's tiny enemies — including the acorn weevil — that would be very difficult to take under natural conditions.*

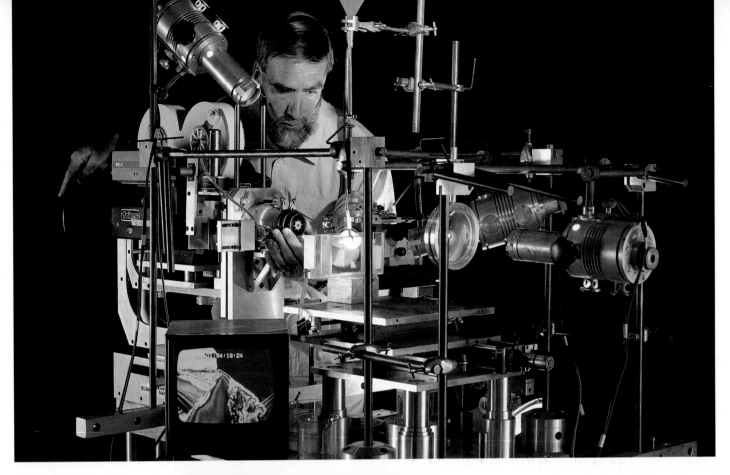

Above & right: *Filming tiny animals, such as plankton, poses almost insuperable problems in the wild and is very difficult even in the studio. But Oxford Scientific Films designed this 'dark field optical bench' to photograph such subjects from different angles, eliminating vibration by linking the camera, mirrors, lights and subject to the same structure.*

Right: *A studio shot freezes a hummingbird darting from flower to flower.*

is that without the studio set, the behaviour of the fish could not have been so closely observed and consequently its immense educational value never realized.

Similar methods were used to film the breeding behaviour of the harvest mouse, a diminutive European mammal that builds its nest among the stems of tall grasses, including wheat. Several miniature 'wheatfields' were recreated inside glass enclosures in the studio, each with internal glass partitions that restricted the animals' activities to the front 20 cm — the camera's focus range. The nest itself had three small apertures cut into the side for the camera lens and lights. Despite all this the mice acclimatized well, and the camera team was able to film them feeding, mating and giving birth inside the tiny woven nest.

The limitation on animals' movements in a restricted studio set is particularly valuable in high-speed stills photography. This technique, pioneered by British photographer, Stephen Dalton, enables an animal, such as an insect or bat, to 'take its own photograph' by flying through a light beam that triggers a camera capable of extremely short, action-freezing exposures. This though is not without its problems as the difficulty is to get the animal to fly through the beam. Butterflies, for example, seem to fly at random in the wild and cannot be relied on to head for a particular spot like, say, a bird returning to its nest. So the answer is to capture the creature and confine it in a dark box with a single exit. Invariably the butterfly will head for the light at the end of the tunnel, passing through the light-beam trigger on the way. The camera shutter opens, the flash fires, and the butterfly — and any foliage or other 'props' arranged in the flight tunnel — are caught on film. All this may seem straightforward, even easy, but the results are often quite unpredictable. To some extent this enhances the interest: the photographer has no idea what has been recorded until the film is developed. The results may be either disastrous or, with luck, show some particular aspect of behaviour or a physical feature that has never been clearly noted before.

Such pictures may be highly 'artificial' yet they are frequently cited amongst the most memorable wildlife images ever made. They are also immensely valuable, not only as scientific and educational documents, but because they provide new glimpses of the awesome beauty to be found everywhere in the natural world.

John Woodward

CAUGHT IN THE ACT

Slow-motion film is taken at very high speed and then played back at normal speed. A film camera normally runs at 24 frames per second (fps), but slow motion may demand 1000 fps or more. Special cameras have to be made to cope with such speed as even a slight malfunction in the film feed could cause the several hundreds of metres of expensive film that zips through the mechanisms to be shredded in seconds. Lighting for high-speed filming also has to be much brighter than normal to compensate for the shortened exposure of each frame. The lights needed for really high-speed work of 3000 fps or more generate so much heat that they can be turned on for only a few seconds at a time. Any longer and they would probably set fire to the set.

To make films that speed up slow events — like flowers unfurling from bud — the film speed is reduced to perhaps one frame every hour or so and the camera may be set up for days on end, linked to a timer that actuates the shutter, film drive and lights for each exposure.

'Freezing' the action in a single shot of an event that happens too quickly to see, like the beating of insects' wings, requires another technique. For this work, exposures of around 1/25,000 second are needed. An in-camera shutter is incapable of this, so the subject is lit with electronic flash units that discharge ultra-short bursts of high-intensity light and a special rapid shutter mechanism is attached to the front of the lens to capture the image. Triggering camera and flash by hand at exactly the right moment is virtually impossible, so the equipment is usually fired automatically when the subject flies through a beam of infra-red light.

A multiple-image of a green lacewing showing its extraordinary vertical take-off: a previously unrecognized feat of aerial agility captured in the studio by Stephen Dalton in the course of some 900 exposures.

AN INTERVIEW WITH
BILL ODDIE

Above: *Bill Oddie birdwatching on his favourite home patch — Hampstead Heath in London.*

Right: *Bill's ideal bird-watching site is an island, preferably off Scotland, where seabirds and spring falls of migrants provide spectacular viewing.*

Opposite: *Egg stealing is illegal in the UK but the breeding success of rare birds of prey, especially breeding visitors such as the osprey, is continually put under threat by determined collectors.*

Not many conservationists have silver discs for record sales on their wall. But then not many conservationists lead the varied kind of life that Bill Oddie enjoys. He has starred in a classic TV comedy series — *The Goodies* — and he has hit the Top Ten; The Goodies' record *Funky Gibbon* reached Number 4 in March 1975. He appears in TV commercials: advertising everything from breakfast cereal to nappies; he has even been the voice of a strawberry! But Bill Oddie's consuming, life-long interest is not the stage, screen and bright lights: it is birds.

Bill began his birdwatching career at an early age, but not in a way you might have expected of one now so keen on conservation. 'I've got a terrible confession to make, I'm afraid. I was a juvenile egg-collector. I spent the early part of my childhood in Rochdale, a northern town, very industrial and not well-known for its wildlife. Even so, like all towns, it did have its birds. I remember the first nest I found — a dunnock's — in the hedge right in front of our terraced house; and from then on I became absorbed by birds and their eggs.

'I suppose I was about 6 or 7 at the time and though it was naughty and delinquent, I did have a kind of code of conduct which I shared with the few other young collectors who I happened to meet: you would only take one egg, and you'd take it early in the season so the bird had time to lay again and replace it.'

Bill's egg-collecting career, however, soon came to a fairly traumatic end. 'I happened to find a pheasant's nest on a golf course. It was very wet and the eggs were stone cold — it had obviously been abandoned. When I got home I tried to "blow" the egg so that it could take its place in my collection. I blew and blew, but it was so old and caked inside that nothing came out. Being delinquent and stupid in those days I actually sucked instead: sure enough it all came out — in my mouth! I can still taste bad eggs when I think of it.'

The experience was a turning point. Bill immediately transferred his attentions from eggs to the birds which laid them. 'Egg collecting's illegal today, and I'm glad of that, though unfortunately people do still do it. Ironically it tends to be adults rather than youngsters now, which is a bit bizarre.' Birds of prey, such as peregrine falcons, are particularly at risk from egg-collectors, who take eggs to hatch and rear the young. There are still people who collect eggs for the sake of collecting. It may not be as important as habitat destruction, but even so, egg-collecting is one of the many threats facing birds in the modern world.

As Bill's interest in birds developed over the years, he became drawn to particular places. 'My favourite type of place is a small island, and my favourite bird holiday is to be on an island for a certain amount of time and keep a log of everything I see. I love the Shetlands, especially islands like Out Skerries or Fair Isle, where there's very little cover. If you get a fall of birds at migration time in spring or autumn it can be truly spectacular, with birds virtually dropping out of the sky. By the evening you just don't know where to look, there's so much to see.' Bill visited the Shetlands again early in 1993, but not for a holiday. It was immediately after the wreck of the oil-tanker *Braer*, and he was reporting on the damage caused by the massive oil spill. Rough weather dispersed the oil quite quickly, but as Bill points out, not quickly enough, for many seabirds still died; 'It worries

Above: *Anything for a good cause — especially if it involves birds.*

Right & below: *Bill noted all three species of British woodpecker in the same day on Hampstead Heath.*

me a great deal. We need to have much stronger laws on pollution. Economic pressures mean that some oil companies run their boats as cheaply as possible, and that means that the wrong kinds of boats are carrying oil, and carrying it in places where there is danger of pollution having a devastating effect.'

But this particular cloud does have a silver lining; at least there was instant media interest in the fate of the birds and other wildlife and Bill has no doubt that this is good for wider involvement: 'Getting people involved in bird-watching can definitely help conservation efforts. The biggest lesson of all is that it's enjoyable. It's all very well trying to get people to support conservation simply because it's a good cause, but if people

watch and enjoy birds they are naturally going to care about protecting them. The more people who passionately care about birds the more conservation as a whole will benefit — if you protect the birds you get a knock-on effect; everything is inter-linked and everything benefits.

'In the end, the world is run by governments and large industries. The more people in positions of power who are also birdwatchers, botanists or wildlife enthusi-asts of any sort, the safer the natural world will be. I'm glad to say that I've met a lot of people in very large companies in world-affecting industries like oil and chemicals who are genuinely keen on birds. I haven't met so many interested politicians, I'm sorry to say, but there's always hope.'

Bill feels that the interests of business people, and the fact that birdwatching itself is becoming a bigger and bigger business, can be a force for good. 'I can give a perfect example of that', he says. 'The annual Bird Race: it's supported by

the big binocular makers, and it raises a lot of money for conservation projects. The races are enormous fun, with 100 or more sponsored teams bombing around their own counties for 24 hours trying to see as many different birds as possible. The end result is hard cash going to conservation projects.' In recent years money has gone to help establish new reserves in Poland for species like the spotted eagle, and to help save what remains of the once extensive Spanish steppes, the mosaic of traditional farmland and wild grasslands that is one of the last strongholds of the great bustard.

As a well-known media personality, Bill can use his standing to help spread the message of conservation. 'I enjoy the positive aspects. I do look for opportunities to help, whether it's opening a new nature reserve or fighting against a development that threatens an important wildlife site. I get requests every week, and, of course, I can't do everything, but I do try to concentrate on the things I can help with.'

He believes that TV has an important role to play in increasing people's interest in birds, and as a seasoned media professional himself, he feels that TV wildlife programmes could be doing more. He wishes that there was more shown about the actual hobby itself — about the pleasures (and pains) of birdwatching. He has been trying to get such a programme off the ground for a good few years now, and hopes that it might eventually happen.

The increasing number of people who are taking up birding pleases Bill, and he has a few handy hints for novices. 'For a start, it's easy. Nowadays you can pick and choose between a whole range of field guides; there weren't any when I started. I do hope that parents are there to help. If a kid is showing an interest, parents can at least try to buy them a decent pair of binoculars, which are hard to afford on pocket money. Parents can help with transport, too, when there's a chance to watch birds at weekends or on holidays. I was fortunate that my dad did that; though he had no interest in birds whatsoever he did help, and made it easier for me. What's more, you won't be regarded as some kind of freak nowadays; you were in my day, and you had to go around desperately trying to find secret friends who also admitted that they were birdwatchers. There are plenty of clubs to join, where you can share interests and go to places together — there are local clubs and, of course, national ones, like the RSPB's Young Ornithologists' Club. Get your own patch — your garden, or the school grounds — and start to identify the common birds.

'A really practical way to get to know birds is through their calls. It can be baffling at first, but as you get to know their voices you soon start to tell when there is something unusual about, often long before you see it. Don't get into the rare bird obsession straight away — get to know the common birds and the rarities will come later of their own accord. But watch out for the great tit; it can make its call sound like just about anything.' A talent for which Bill is just as well known!

Dr Tony Hare

Above: Bill's place on The Goodies' *bicycle earned lots of laughs in their TV comedy series; now he wants to use the bike for a more serious purpose — riding the length of India's holy River Ganges to arouse a wider concern for its heavily polluted waters which are home to rare species like the Ganges susu, a freshwater dolphin.*

Below: Bill's advice to birdwatching newcomers; '... try to get to know the easy, common species first, and then if you can't recognize a magpie, take up train-spotting!'

DIRECTORY OF ORGANIZATIONS

GLOBAL ORGANIZATIONS AND INITIATIVES

Ark Environmental Foundation
PO Box 18
Melbourne
Royston
Hertfordshire SG8 6JQ
© 071 409 2638
Provides information and a framework for community action to benefit the natural environment.

BirdLife International
Wellbrook Court
Girton Road
Cambridge CB3 ONA
© 0223 277318
Campaigns to protect the world's birds and habitats.

Council of Europe
Centre Naturopa
Conseil de l'Europe
BP 431 R 6
F 67006 Strasbourg
France
© 010 33 88 61 49 61
Steering committee for Conservation and Management of the Environment and Natural Resources throughout Europe.

Environmental Investigation Agency
2nd Floor
2 Peartree Court
London EC1R ODS
© 071 490 7040
A non-profitmaking investigative organization working to protect wildlife and the environment throughout the world.

European Commission DG X1 (Environment)
Division B3 EC
Rue de la Loi 200
1049 Brussels
Belgium
Responsible for European Community environmental policy.

Fauna and Flora Preservation Society
Kensington Gore
London SW7 2AR
© 071 823 8899
Promotes the conservation of wild animals and plants worldwide.

Friends of the Earth International
Veriniging Milieudefensie
Tacovanden Heiligenberg
Damrak 26
1012 LJ
Amsterdam. The Netherlands
© 010 31 20 622 1386
Campaigns vigorously for the protection of the environment and sustainable alternative sources of fuel and economic practices.

Gaia Foundation
18 Well Walk
London NW3 1LD
© 071 435 5000
Provides funding to support indigenous populations, mainly in the South American rainforests.

Greenpeace International
Keizersgracht 176
1016 DW Amsterdam
The Netherlands
© 010 31 205 236555
Campaigns against abuse of the environment through lobbying and non-violent direct action.

Institute for European Environmental Policy
158 Buckingham Palace Road
London SW1W 9TR
© 071 824 8787
Analyzes and reports on environmental policy throughout Europe.

Institute of Terrestrial Ecology
Monks Wood
Abbots Ripton
Huntingdon
Cambridgeshire PE17 2LS
© 04873 381
Researches ecosystems, surveys land use and environmental problem areas.

International Foundation for the Conservation of Birds
11300 Weddington St
North Hollywood
California 91601 USA
Campaigns to conserve birds in the USA and worldwide.

International Primate Protection League
116 Judd Street
London WC1H 9NS
© 071 837 7227
Works exclusively to protect primates worldwide

International Waterfowl and Wetlands Research Bureau
Slimbridge
Gloucestershire GL2 7BT
© 0453 890634
Promotes research and conservation of wetlands.

International Wildlife Coalition
PO Box 73
Hartfield
Sussex TN7 4EY
© 0342 825482
Promotes research into wildlife and natural habitat destruction.

People's Trust for Endangered Species
Suite 9
Hamble House
Mead Row
Godalming
Surrey GU7 3JX
© 0483 424848
Environmental conservation by the protection of animals, plants and wild places.

Population Concern
231 Tottenham Court Road
London W1P 9AE
© 071 631 1546
Independent charity working to promote awareness of global population issues.

Rainforest Foundation
2 Ingate Place
Battersea
London SW8 3NS
© 071 498 7603
Works in partnership with native Amazonians to preserve tropical rainforest.

Society for Wildlife Art of the Nations
Wallsworth Hall
Twigworth
Gloucestershire GL2 9PA
© 0452 731422
Aims to link artists with conservation.

Survival International
310 Edgware Road
London W2 1DY
© 071 723 5535
Works for the rights of tribal peoples worldwide.

Tusk
115 Ebury Street
London SW1W 9QU
© 071 823 6040
Conducts African wildlife projects with special interests in elephants and rhinos.

World Conservation Monitoring Centre
219c Huntingdon Road
Cambridge CB3 0DL
© 0223 277314
Collects and disseminates information on animals and plants.

World Conservation Union (IUCN)
Rue Mauverney 28
1196 Gland
Geneva
Switzerland
© 010 41 223 9114
Independent alliance of over 120 countries uniting on equal terms to tackle conservation.

World Wide Fund for Nature International
1196 Gland
Geneva
Switzerland
© 010 41 223 7181
Campaigns for conservation of wildlife and wild places.

Worldwatch Institute
1776 Massachusetts Avenue NW
Washington DC20036 USA
© 010 1 202 452 1999
Informs governments and the public of environmental issues.

UK ORGANIZATIONS
General

Amateur Entomologists Society
22 Salisbury Road
Feltham
Middlesex TW13 5DP
© 081 890 3584
Promotes the study of all insects.

Association for the Protection of Rural Scotland
Gladstone's Land
483 Lawnmarket
Edinburgh EH1 2NT
© 031 225 7013
Informs and influences public opinion on Scotland's countryside.

Barn Owl Trust
Waterleat
Ashburton
Devon TQ13 7HU
℡ 0364 53026
Works to conserve the barn owl and preserve its natural habitat.

Bat Conservation Trust
London Ecology Centre
45 Shelton Street
London WC2H 9HJ
℡ 071 240 0933
Conducts research and projects to increase public awareness of bats.

Bird Line (Bird Information Service)
Stonerunner
Coast Road
Cley-next-the-Sea, Holt
Norfolk NR25 7RZ
℡ 0263 741139
Telephone service on the status of all rare birds in the UK.

Botanical Society of the British Isles
C/o Department of Botany
Natural History Museum
Cromwell Road
London SW7 5BD
℡ 071 589 6323 Ex8701
Encourages the study and conservation of plants.

British Butterfly Conservation Society
P O Box 222
Dedham
Colchester
Essex CO7 6EY
℡ 0509 412870
Sponsors the study and protection of butterflies.

British Divers Marine Life Rescue
Mayland Road
Corby
Northamptonshire NN17 2DR
℡ 0536 201511
A rescue society for marine mammals.

British Herpetological Society
C/o London Zoo
Regent's Park
London NW1 4RY
℡ 071 722 3333
Promotes the study of reptiles and amphibians.

British Naturalists Association
48 Russell Way
Higham Ferrers
Northamptonshire NN9 8EJ
℡ 0933 314672
Promotes the protection and study of natural history and landscapes.

British Trust for Conservation Volunteers
36 St Mary's Street
Wallingford
Oxfordshire OX10 0EU
℡ 0491 39766
Organizes practical conservation work for volunteers of all ages.

British Trust for Ornithology
The Nunnery
Nunnery Place
Thetford
Norfolk IP24 2PU
℡ 0842 750050
Promotes the serious study of British wild birds.

British Wildlife Rehabilitation Council
c/o RSPCA (address below)
Functions as a forum for rehabilitators to exchange views and information on caring for wildlife.

Care for the Wild
1 Ashfolds
Horsham Road
Rusper
West Sussex RH12 4QX
℡ 0293 871596
Works to alleviate cruelty to, and suffering of, wildlife.

The Conservation Trust
George Palmer Site
Northumberland Avenue
Reading
Berkshire RG2 7PW
℡ 0734 868442
A public environmental information and education service.

Council for the Protection of Rural England (CPRE)
Warwick House
25 Buckingham Palace Road
London SW1W 0PP
℡ 071 976 6433
Promotes the improvement and protection of the English rural countryside.

Campaign for the Protection of Rural Wales
Ty Gwyn
31 High Street
Welshpool
Powys SY21 7JP
℡ 0938 552525
Promotes the improvement and protection of the rural Welsh countryside.

The Country Trust
Denham Hill Farmhouse
Quainton
Aylesbury
Buckinghamshire HP22 4AN
℡ 0296 641708
Conducts visits to the countryside for inner city children.

Countryside Commission
John Dower House
Crescent Place
Cheltenham
Gloucestershire GL50 3RA
℡ 0242 521381
Advises central/local government on rural conservation and recreation.

Countryside Council for Wales
Plas Penrhos
Penrhos Road
Bangor
Gwynedd LL57 2LQ
℡ 0248 370444
Organization replacing the Countryside Commission and Nature Conservancy Council in Wales.

Countryside Education Trust
John Montagu Building
Beaulieu
Hampshire SO42 7ZN
℡ 0590 612340
Works to make the countryside accessible to all and promotes caring attitude.

Countryside Venture
Lime Tree
Asherington, Totnes
Devon TQ9 7UL
℡ 0803 732562
Training centres for practical management and rural skills.

Department of the Environment (Wildlife Division)
Tollgate House
Houlton Street
Bristol
Avon BS2 9DJ
℡ 0272 218233
Responsible for zoos, environmental education, species conservation, and trade in endangered species.

Department of the Environment for Northern Ireland
Calvert House
23 Castle Place
Belfast BT1 1FY
℡ 0232 230560
Responsible for the conservation of wildlife and the environment and for the designation of important areas.

Durrell Institute of Conservation and Ecology
University of Kent
Canterbury CT2 7NX
℡ 0227 475480
Undertakes research and teaching in conservation biology.

Earthwatch Europe
Belsyre Court
57 Woodstock Road
Oxford OX2 6HU
℡ 0865 311600
Organizes 'green' holidays which allow members of the public to participate in research and field studies.

Elefriends
Coldharbour
Dorking
Surrey RH5 6HA
℡ 0306 713320
Conservation and protection of elephants.

English Nature
Northminster House
Peterborough PE1 1UA
℡ 0733 340345
Government organization which replaced former NCC

Farming and Wildlife Advisory Group
Stoneleigh
Kenilworth
Warwickshire CV8 2RX
℡ 0203 696699
Promotes the conservation of wildlife within the farmed countryside.

Field Studies Council
Preston Montford
Montford Bridge
Shrewsbury
Shropshire SY4 1HW
℡ 0743 850674
Appreciation of the environment and its wildlife through education.

Fish Conservation Centre
Easter Cringate
Stirling FK7 9QX
℡ 0786 51312
Research and practical management projects for fish conservation.

Forestry Commission
231 Corstorphine Road
Edinburgh EH12 7AT
℡ 031 334 0303
National forestry authority in the UK, it also offers advice to private foresters.

Friends of the Earth
26-28 Underwood Street
London N1 7JQ
℡ 071 490 1555
Works to promote policy changes that conserve the natural environment.

Greenpeace (UK)
Canonbury Villas
London N1 2PN
℡ 071 354 5100
Campaigns against abuse of the environment through direct action.

The Hawk and Owl Trust
C/o Birds of Prey Section
Zoological Society of London
Regent's Park
London NW1 4RY
Conserves and encourages the study of birds of prey.

Hydestyle Wildlife Hospital
Nutwood Cottage
New Road
Hydestyle, Godalming
Surrey GU8 4DJ
℡ 0483 860313
Front line experts in wild animal care.

International Tree Foundation
Sandy Lane
Crawley Down
West Sussex RH10 4HS
℡ 0342 712536
Worldwide tree planting and protection society.

Irish Wildbird Conservancy
Ruttledge House
8 Longford Place
Monkstown
County Dublin
✆ 010 3531 280 4322
Promotes study and conservation of wild birds in Ireland.

League Against Cruel Sports
83-87 Union Street
London SE1 1SG
✆ 071 403 6155
Campaigns against sports which cause suffering to animals.

Living Earth
The Old Laundry
Ossington Buildings
Moxon Street
London W1M 3JD
✆ 071 487 3661
Promotes conservation through education.

Lynx
PO Box 509
Great Dunmow
Essex CM6 1UH
✆ 0371 872016
Campaigns against the killing of animals for their fur.

Mammal Society
C/o Department of Zoology
University of Bristol
Woodlands Road
Bristol BS8 1UG
✆ 0272 272300
Promotes the study and conservation of mammals.

Marine Biological Association of the United Kingdom
The Plymouth Marine Laboratory
Citadel Hill
Plymouth
Devon PL1 2PB
✆ 0752 222772
Promotes scientific research into marine biology; runs the Marine Pollution information Centre.

Marine Conservation Society
9 Gloucester Road
Ross-on-Wye
Herefordshire HR9 5BU
✆ 0989 66017
Campaigns to protect and conserve the wildlife of the coast and offshore waters.

The Monkey Sanctuary
Looe
Cornwall PL13 1NZ
✆ 0503 262532
Provides a home for a colony of grey woolly monkeys, offers advice about keeping monkeys in captivity: has a rehabilitation project to reintroduce species to Amazonia.

National Birds of Prey Centre
Newent
Gloucestershire GL18 1JJ
✆ 0531 820286
Has a successful captive breeding collection of raptors and advises other zoos in the breeding of endangered species.

7 London Road
Tetbury
Gloucestershire GL8 8JQ
✆ 0666 503419
Work for conservation of badgers.

National Rivers Authority
Eastbury House
30-34 Albert Embankment
London SE1 7TL
✆ 071 820 0101
Watchdog with powers to oversee water quality in the UK.

National Trust for Scotland
5 Charlotte Square
Edinburgh EH2 4DU
✆ 031 226 5922
Works to preserve land and buildings of national interest in Scotland.

New Quay Bird & Wildlife Hospital
Penfoel
Cross Inn
Llandysul
Dyfed SA44 6NR
✆ 0545 560462
Wildlife hospital specializing in the care of wild birds.

Otter Trust
Earsham
Nr Bungay
Suffolk NR35 2AF
✆ 0986 893470
Protects and conserves otters, especially the European otter.

Owl Study Group
The Nunnery
Nunnery Place
Thetford
Norfolk IP24 2PU
✆ 0842 750050
Forum for exchange of ideas for those interested in owls.

Plantlife
Natural History Museum
Cromwell Road
London SW7
✆ 071 938 9111
Works for protection of plants in the UK and worldwide and helps recreate lost habitats.

Rare Breeds Survival Trust
National Agricultural Centre
Kenilworth
Warwickshire CV8 2LG
✆ 0203 696551
Aims to increase the numbers of rare breeds, keeps breeding registers. provides funds and holds workshops.

Reptile Protection Trust
College Gates
2 Deansway
Worcester WR1 2JD
✆ 0483 417550
Works for the conservation of reptiles.

Royal Society for Nature Conservation
The Wildlife Trusts Partnership
The Green
Witham Park
Waterside South
Lincoln LN5 7JR
✆ 0522 544400
The umbrella group for the many local and county-based conservation trusts.

Royal Society for the Prevention of Cruelty to Animals
Causeway
Horsham
West Sussex RH12 1HG
✆ 0403 264181
Promotes kindness to animals and aims to prevent cruelty and suffering.

Royal Society for the Protection of Birds
The Lodge
Sandy
Bedfordshire SG19 2DL
✆ 0767 680551
Conserves and protects wild birds, manages nature reserves, conducts research, surveys and campaigns.

Scott Polar Research Institute
Lenfield Road
Cambridge CB2 1ER
✆ 0223 336540
Research and information service covering polar regions.

Scottish Conservation Projects
Freepost
Stirling SK8 2BR
✆ 0786 79697
Scotland's leading charity involving people in practical conservation.

Scottish Natural Heritage
12 Hope Terrace
Edinburgh EH9 2AS
✆ 031 447 4784
Organization replacing Countryside Commission and Nature Conservancy Council in Scotland.

Scottish Society for the Prevention of Cruelty to Animals
19 Melville Street
Edinburgh EH3 7PL
✆ 031 225 6418
Animal welfare charity dealing with wildlife, livestock and pets.

Scottish Tree Trust
30 Edgemont Street
Glasgow G413EL
✆ 041 649 2462
Works to maintain native woodlands.

Scottish Wildlife Trust
25 Johnstone Terrace
Edinburgh EH1 2NH
✆ 031 445 4198
Works to conserve Scotland's natural flora and fauna.

Sea Shepherd
PO Box 5
Ashford
Middlesex
✆ 0784 254846
Campaigns to conserve all marine wildlife.

Skye Environmental Centre
Broadford
Isle of Skye
Scotland IV49 9AQ
✆ 0471 822487
Wildlife hospital and field study centre.

Tree Council
35 Belgrave Square
London SW1X 8QN
✆ 071 235 8854
Works to improve the environment by the planting and care of trees.

Trust for Urban Ecology
PO Box 514
London SE16 1AS
✆ 071 237 9165
Aims to promote awareness and expertise in urban ecology, habitat creation and wildlife management.

Vale Wildlife Rescue
Station Road
Beckford
Tewksbury
Gloucestershire GL20 7AN
✆ 0386 882288

Voluntary Service Overseas
317 Putney Bridge Road
London SW15 2PN
✆ 081 780 1331
Organizes voluntary work worldwide.

Wader Study Group
44 The Pastures
Edlesborough
Dunstable
Beds. LU6 2HL
An association of ornithologists interested in wading birds.

Whale and Dolphin Conservation Society
19a James Street West
Bath
Avon BA1 2BT
✆ 0225 334511
Works for the conservation of whales and dolphins.

Wildfowl and Wetlands Centre
Martin Mere
Burscough
Ormskirk
Lancashire L40 0TA
✆ 0704 895181
Sanctuary for injured and orphaned birds.

Wildfowl and Wetlands Trust
Slimbridge
Gloucestershire GL2 7BT
℡ 0453 890333
Works to conserve and study the world's wildfowl and their natural habitats.

Wildlife Hospitals Trust
St Tiggywinkles
Aston Road
Haddenham
Buckinghamshire HP17 8AF
℡ 0844 292292
Takes in and treats all British wild animals. Educates others in their care and treatment.

Wildlife Sound Recording Society
National Sound Archive
29 Exhibition Road
London SW7 2AS
℡ 071 589 6603
Provides help and advice on recording wildlife sounds.

Woodlands Trust
Autumn Park
Dysart Road
Grantham
Lincolnshire NG31 6LL
℡ 0476 74297
Works for the conservation of broadleaved and native British trees and the creation of new woodlands.

World Wide Fund for Nature UK
Panda House
Weyside Park
Godalming
Surrey GU7 1XR
℡ 0483 426444
Campaigns to conserve natural resources and promote sustainable activity through education, training and the conservation of species.

Zoo Check
Coldharbour
Dorking
Surrey RH5 6HA
℡ 0306 712091
Monitors zoo conditions in the UK and works to raise standards of captive animal care.

POLITICAL GROUPS

Green Alliance
60 Chandos Place
London WC2N 4HG
℡ 071 836 0341
Encourages ecological awareness through all political life in the UK.

Green Democrats (formerly the Liberal Ecology Group)
19a Earls Court Square
London SW5 9BY
℡ 071 373 4631
Works to raise environmental and ecological issues within the Liberal Democratic party.

Green Party
10 Station Parade
Balham High Road
London SW12 9AZ
℡ 081 673 0045
Campaigns to promote harmony with nature and and the practice of sustainable economic activity.

Tory Green Initiative
1 Margaret Street
London W1N 7LG
℡ 071 580 4433
Informs MPs and others of developments in the international ecology movement.

FOR CHILDREN

Go Wild Club
PO Box 101
Wetherby
Yorkshire LS23 6EE
℡ 0937 541542
Junior branch of the WWF for members aged 7-18.

Mammal Society Youth Group
C/o Department of Zoology
University of Bristol
Woodlands Road
Bristol BS8 1UG
℡ 0272 272300
Seeks to promote an interest in mammals, mainly for the under 18s.

Raleigh International
The Power House
Alpha Place
Flood Street
London SW3 5SZ
℡ 071 351 7541
An international charity which organizes conservation and community projects.

Watch Trust for Environmental Education Ltd
The Green
Witham Park
Waterside South
Lincoln LN2 2NR
℡ 0552 544400
Run by the RSNC to enable young people to learn about wildlife and to take an active part in conservation.

Young People's Trust for the Environment & Nature Conservation
95 Woodbridge Road
Guildford
Surrey GU1 4PY
℡ 0483 39600
An education and information service, especially for schools.

Young Ornithologists Club (YOC)
The Lodge
Sandy
Bedfordshire SG19 2DL
℡ 0767 680551
The junior branch of the RSPB. Applicants must be under the age of 16 to join, but can remain in the YOC until 18.

ACKNOWLEDGEMENTS

Adrian Barnett *(MA Oxon, MSc)* is a freelance writer who has worked in the rainforests of Africa, South America and South-east Asia. Over the past decade he has discovered several new and long-lost species.
Niall Benvie *(MA)* is a photographer and writer based in Scotland. In 1992 he won the 'Birds Behaviour' section of the British Gas Wildlife Photographer of the Year competition.
John Birdsall *(BSc)* is a freelance author and editor specializing in wildlife and conservation topics.
Hanna Bolus *(MA Oxon)* is a freelance editor and writer on international environmental issues.
Duncan Brewer is a full-time writer whose specializations include natural history, earth sciences, Third World issues and investigative journalism.
Alison Byard is a committed environmentalist who currently works for the Wildfowl and Wetlands Trust.

Jonathan Elphick *(BSc)* is a natural history editor, consultant and author with a special interest in ornithology, who is currently working on a multi-media project for the BBC.
Sarah Foster *(BA)* is a journalist with a special interest in the environment. An experienced scuba diver, she has recently spent five months in South America where she was involved in marine conservation work.
Jeff Hall is a writer, photographer, professional tour guide and whale researcher, working in Alaska, California, Baja California and the mountains and deserts of the southwestern USA.
Dr Tony Hare is an ecologist and communicator who has produced numerous natural history TV programmes, books and articles and is chairman of the board of Plantlife, the plant conservation charity.

John Hechtel is a specialist in bear behaviour, ecology and conservation who has worked for the Alaska Department of Fish and Game for over 17 years. He is also a writer and photographer and has advised on TV documentaries for the BBC and National Geographic.
Suzanne Jones *(BA)* is a writer and editor who has recently been involved with the *Wildlife Fact-File*.
Fred Pearce is an environmental journalist and author specializing in international issues. He is an author of books on acid rain, the greenhouse effect and environmental campaigning.
Chris Pellant *(BA)* is a lecturer, writer and photographer specializing in earth sciences and natural history.
Douglas Richardson has over 18 years experience working in zoos and currently manages the carnivore collection at at London Zoo where he is involved in the Asian Lion Conservation Programme.

Michael Scott *(BSc, Dip Ed)* is a writer and broadcaster on wildlife and conservation, who also edits and publishes *SCENES*, the Scottish Environmental Newsletter.
Tony Stones *(BSc, MSc)* trained as an ecologist and has worked for the RSPB as a freelance environmentalist, acting as the principal contributor to the publication *Important Bird Areas in the UK*.
Colin Tudge is a zoologist who works as a writer and broadcaster, mainly for *New Scientist* and the BBC.
Matthew Turner *(BA)* is a writer and editor who has recently contributed to the *Wildlife Fact-File*.
Dr Sally Uren *(BSc, Phd)* has carried out detailed research on South-east Asian rainforests and presently works as an environmental consultant.
John Woodward *(BA)* is a freelance writer and photographer with a particular penchant for insects and spiders.

PICTURE CREDITS

Abbreviations:
t – top; b – bottom; l – left; r – right

Bryan & Cherry Alexander
66, 67b,72t, 76, 81br

All Action Pictures
A Shaw 198t

Animals Animals/Earth Scenes
B P Kent 189t, J Lemker 168t, T Levin 113t, S Moore 132, J Pontier 173t, C Roessler 19, Stouffer Prodctions Ltd 185t

Ardea London Ltd
I Beames, 41b, 167tl, J P Ferrero 35t, 89tr, Ferrero/Labat 33, 98, K W Fink 36b, B Gibbons 153, F Gohier 60, 61t, 63, 71t, 170t, C Haagner 141, A Lindau 34br, P Morris 61b, P Nesent 49, J Swedberg 65, 96br, 96tl, V Taylor 20br, 22b, 24tr, 24b

Peter Arnold Inc
N Duplaix 11bl

André Bartschi
175

© BBC Photograph Library
199t

Bird Life
G Stiles 39b

British Antarctic Survey
C Gilbert 118

Laurie Campbell
177b

Ray Charter
12t

Chester Zoo
34tl

Bruce Coleman Ltd
E & P Bauer 52b, 94ctl, N Blake 199b, J Burton 28tr, 31tr, R Campbell 14tr, J Cancalosi 172b, 62b, A Compost 46, 94cbl, 14b, G Cubitt 14b, A Davies 155bl, N de Vore 99b, G Dore 95tr, F J Erize 91br, J Fennekk 58bl, M Fogden 140t, 170b, J Foott 78b, 85, C Frith 145tr, K Gunnar 62t, C James 154, J Johnson 64, S Krasemann 99t, G Langsbury 84tl, W Lankinen 94tl, L Lyon 17bl, McCarthy 101t, 94bl, M McKavett 140b, F Mercay 32b, G Plage 31bl, J Rydell 169l, J Shaw 80t, J Taylor 45, K Taylor 51, Williams 145b, G Zeisler 11t, 15br, C Zuber 54, A Zuckerman 47t

Collections
B Shuel 198br

Dinodia Picture Library
© J Mehta 16l

Earthwatch Europe
J Howell 161b, J Mahler 161t, Morrissey/Gruber 162b, N Rowe 160tl, R Schleipman 158, 163bl, 163br

Environmental Investigation Agency
128t, 128b, 131bl, 131br

© Gerry Ellis
182tr

Environmental Picture Library
I Lengui 90bl, A McCarthy 88tl

Falklands Conservation
T Stones 84tr

First Light
© S Homer 76t, 79b, © 1987 W Wegner78t

Frank Lane Picture Agency
D Greycock 95br, J Hawkins 135, Hosking E 62t, F Newman 75tr, M Newman 94tr, 97tr, Silvestris 130, R Wilmshurst 102tl

Geoff Franklin
148t

© 1988 Winston Fraser
81b

Louis Miguel Ruiz Gordon
182b

Greenpeace
Beltra 92, Hodson 94cc

Jeff C Hall
169tr

Gerald Hide
179tr

Hydestile Wildlife Hospital
T Anderson 146, 151

ICCE
M Depraz 88b

The Image Bank
C Brandsetter 120t, B Mitchell122b

Thomas D Mangelsen
80b

© Bill Ivy
27

Jacana
J P Ferrero 48bl, 42, J Hellio/N Van Ingen 137b, J P Varin 47b, P Wild 138t

Jan Tove Johansson
181b

Manfred Klindwort
8

© Ted Levin
77l, 77br, 79t

© Richard Longseth
186br, 187t

Peter P Marra
40b

Neil McIntyre
174bl

H Lyn Miles, Project Chantek
44t, 44b

© John Eastcott/ Yva Momatiuk
J Eastcott 180b

Charles A Munn III
38t, 38b

Nature Photographers Ltd
P Sterry 30t, 31cr

National Park Services
J Smith 172t

© National Trust 1991
R Hallet 155cr, N Meers 157tr, M Trelawny 157bl

NHPA (Nattural History Photographic Agency)
B & C Alexander 67t, 67bl. 71b, ANT 53b, S Dalton, 26t, 193tl, 195br, 198bl, N Dennis 133t, P Fagot43, G Gainsburgh 152, Rao E Hanumantha 28b, B Jones 95bl, S Krasemann 68b, 70b, G Lacz 69, J Meech 29br, J Shaw 68t, M Tweedie 138b

New Quay Bird & Wildlife Hospital
149r

Natural Science Photos
D B Fleetham 11br, M Harvey 133b, 131t, 129, L Hes 12b

Oxford Scientific Films
F Bavendam 39t, G I Bernard 101bl, 190l, 190r, A Carey 173b, J Cooney 100t, S Dalton 195bl, J Foott 84b, R Gemmell 193cr, H Hall 6, M Hamblin 156b, R Jackman 167b, M Koretz 194l, L Lauber 101br, M Leach 103tr, T McHugh 37b, 91bl, B Osborne 97cr, S Osolinski 139, 171, 82b, 82t, R Packwood 26b, J Paling 192t, 192b, P Parks 194b, K Sandved 55b, A Shay 191, T Shepherd 193b, M Stouffer 102cl, T Tilford 55t, 136b, T Ulrich 100cl, A Walsh 148b, K Wothe 83

Richard Packwood
182cl

Rob Palmer
104, 105, 106, 107b, 107t, 107c, 108, 109t

Panos Pictures
P Harrison 123b

Keijo Pentinen
180tr

Photo Researchers Inc
D Faulkner 115, F Gohier 110, P Leeson 116b, W Partington 114b, 114t

Planet Earth Pictures
J Brandenberg 70t, G Douwma 23l, J Downer 127 tl, Eastcott/Momamatiuk 52tr, N Greaves 102tr, F Kristo 159, R Matthews 36t, P Palmer 103b, D Perrine 20tl, 22t, 127b, A Shah 14tl, 16tr, M Snyderman 23r, J D Watt 21tr, 164, N Wu 20bl

Samantha Purdy
183

RSPB
C Gomersall 155t, 156t, M W Richards 197b

Scope Features
196tl

Scotland in Focus
W S Paton 197tr

Gregory K Scott
188tr

Colin Seddon
147t, 147b, 149b

Science Photo Library
S Fraser 93t, P Menzel 122t

Frank Spooner Pictures
A Ribeiro/Gamma 96bl, Van der Stockt/Gamma 93b

The State Historical Society of Wisconsin
188l

Still Pictures
N Dickinson 86, 91t, M Edwards 88tr, 89br, 90br, 90t, 134, H Girardet 87

David Toney
177t

Tom Stack & Associates
D B Fleetham 18, 116t, C Isenhart 53tr, L Lipsky 117b, J McDonald 17t, B Parker 111, 112, E Robinson 25, J Shaw 113b, T Stack 13, F S Westmoreland 24tl

Tony Stone Images
120b, 121, 4, D Armand 123t, D Bjorn 75b, K Griffiths 119, W Jacobs, 75tl, D Woodfall 94cr

From the Collection of the University of Wisconsin-Madison Archives
184

Vale Wildlife Rescue
149t, 150cl

Joanna van Gruisen
176

VIREO
50, S Holt 136tl

© Kennan Ward
178

Konrad Wothe
179b

WWF International
E Copolla 142b, T Larsen 144, R Le Guen 142t, M Lindhard 145tl, J MacKinnon 40t, S Oppegaard 127tr, K Schafer 143, L Stocker 150b

Zefa-Stockmarket/T van Sant
Geosphere Project Endpapers

VOLUNTEER WORK OPPORTUNITIES WITH WILDLIFE AND CONSERVATION ORGANIZATIONS

	Overseas volunteers	Design and/or illustration	Committee work	Education (with adults and children)	Computers	Fundraising	Leafletting	Recording and surveying	Sales, stalls and fairs	Stewards and wardens	Administration/Office work	Communicating with the public	Campaigning	Practical conservation work	Education (Preparation of materials)	Guided walks	Professional skills	Speaking at lectures	Research
Amateur Entomologists Society										●					●				●
Ark Environmental Foundation			●	●	●	●						●	●	●		●		●	●
British Naturalists Association			●			●		●	●		●						●	●	●
British Trust for Conservation Volunteers											●			●	●				
British Trust for Ornithology		●			●	●		●	●		●				●	●	●	●	●
British Butterfly Conservation Society					●	●		●			●				●			●	●
Care for the Wild								●									●		
Council for the Protection of Rural England					●	●	●		●			●	●	●					
Countryside Education Trust		●			●	●	●	●	●	●	●	●	●	●	●	●		●	
Countryside Venture			●	●	●	●	●	●								●	●		
Earthwatch (Europe)	●																		
Friends of the Earth	●	●			●	●					●				●		●		
Gaia Foundation			●	●	●	●	●					●	●	●		●		●	●
Greenpeace			●		●				●	●		●							
Hawk and Owl Trust				●					●	●									
International Council for Bird Preservation	●	●			●						●							●	●
International Primate Protection League	●			●		●					●	●	●						
Living Earth		●	●		●	●					●					●		●	●
Marine Conservation Society			●	●	●		●			●			●					●	
Men of the Trees				●			●	●						●	●	●			●
National Trust for Scotland				●												●	●		
National Trust Volunteer Unit								●		●	●			●			●	●	
Raleigh International	●	●	●	●	●	●	●	●	●	●	●	●	●	●	●		●	●	●
People's Trust for Endangered Species		●		●		●	●	●											
Plantlife											●				●				
Population Concern				●	●		●	●		●									●
Reptile Protection Trust				●	●	●		●		●									
Royal Society for Nature Conservation		●	●		●	●	●	●		●	●	●	●	●	●	●	●	●	●
Royal Society for the Prevention of Cruelty to Animals		●	●	●	●	●	●	●		●	●	●	●			●		●	●
Royal Society for the Protection of Birds				●							●			●		●			
Scottish Conservation Projects		●			●	●		●				●		●			●		
Sea Shepherd		●			●	●	●	●		●		●	●	●					●
Trust for Urban Ecology		●			●	●		●	●	●			●	●		●	●		
Voluntary Services Overseas	●			●															
Wildlife Hospitals Trust																			
Woodland Trust				●						●									●
Working Weekends on Organic Farms												●							●
World of Water	●	●		●	●						●	●	●	●	●		●	●	●
World Wide Fund for Nature			●	●		●	●			●									
Zoo Check				●	●	●		●				●							

INDEX